THE FUTURE OF INDUSTRIAL RESEARCH

THE FUTURE OF

Industrial Research

PAPERS AND DISCUSSION

STANDARD OIL DEVELOPMENT CO.

19 45

Printed in the United States of America
Second Printing

TABLE OF CONTENTS

||||||||||||||||||||||||||||||||||||||||||||||||||||||||||||||||||||||

INTRODUCTION AND SUMMARY

Frank A. Howard, President of the Standard Oil Development Company and Vice President of Standard Oil Company (N. J.): He was organizer of the research unit of the parent company and its administrative head since its inception in 1919. Engineer, inventor and lawyer, he is retiring after twenty-five years to resume private law practice. He serves on the New York Advisory Board of the Chemical Warfare Service.

PART ONE

THEME: "What should be the guiding principles and objectives for the commercial programs of industrial research and development organizations?"

Chairman: C. F. KETTERING

Charles F. Kettering, Vice President and Director of the General Motors Corporation and General Manager of the General Motors Research Laboratories: The new technical developments for which he has been largely responsible include the Delco starting, lighting, and ignition system for automobiles, Ethyl gasoline (with Thomas Midgley, Jr.) and the high speed two-cycle Diesel engine. Since its creation in 1940 he has been Chairman of the National Inventors' Council, and Chairman of the National Patent Planning Commission, established in 1941. He holds numerous medals and awards as well as honorary degrees from fourteen different educational institutions.

Table of Contents

Frank B. Jewett, Vice President of American Telephone and Telegraph Company in charge of development and research, 1925-1944, and Chairman of the Board of the Bell Telephone Laboratories, Inc.: He retired on September 30th of last year. As President of the National Academy of Sciences since 1939, he helped in the formation of the National Defense Research Committee of the Office of Scientific Research and Development, and is now devoting full time to these interests and to allied war research activities.

Thomas Midgley, Jr. : This is the last paper presented by Dr. Midgley before his death on November 2, 1944. At the time of his death he was President and Chairman of the Board of the American Chemical Society. He had been Vice President of the Ethyl Corporation since 1923. He was also Vice President of Kinetic Chemicals, Inc. and a director of the Ethyl-Dow Chemical Company. His discovery of the anti-knock properties of tetraethyl lead and his work on air-conditioning refrigerants had far-reaching effects. His many honors included the Nichols, Longstreth, Perkin, Priestly and Willard Gibbs Medals. From 1940 until his death he served as Vice Chairman of the National Inventors' Council.

Harry L. Derby, President of the American Cyanamid & Chemical Corporation: He is a member of the Board of Conservation and Development of the State of New Jersey and the New Jersey Commisson on Postwar Economic Welfare. He was an Industry Member of the National War Labor Board; is Chairman of the Chemical Advisory Committee of the Army and Navy Munitions Board; President of the Manufacturing Chemists' Association of the United States; and Honorary Vice President and Director of the National Association of Manufacturers. He is a Life Trustee of Rutgers University.

Colonel Bradley Dewey, President of the Dewey & Almy Chemical Company : He served as Deputy Rubber Director of the War Production Board in 1942-43 and as Director until his voluntary liquidation of the agency on September 1st of last year. With the Chemical Warfare Service in World War I, he received the Distinguished Service Medal. In World War II he has been again associated with the C.W.S. as a member of the American Chemical Society's Advisory Committee, and has also served as a member of the Advisory Committee of the Quartermaster Corps.

Table of Contents

PART TWO

THEME: "How can small business serve itself and be served by industrial research and development?"

Chairman: WARREN K. LEWIS

Warren K. Lewis, Professor of Chemical Engineering: He has been on the faculty of the Massachusetts Institute of Technology since 1910, and was the guiding spirit in its Research Laboratory of Applied Chemistry, which, through the period between the two world wars was one of the leading scientific research agencies used by small business. As a consultant for the oil industry, Dr. Lewis has been also a major influence in the scientific revolution in petroleum refining through this same period.

Edwin H. Land, President of the Polaroid Corporation, founder and inventor : He has guided his enterprise from a small research laboratory in the early '30s to a full-fledged industry geared to war production. For his work in the field of polarized light and optics, he has received honors including the Hood, Cresson and John Scott Medals and the Modern Pioneer Award.

Westbrook Steele, Executive Director of the Institute of Paper Chemistry, Lawrence College, Appleton, Wis.: He has been engaged in the educational field since 1921 when he became Vice President of Western Theological Seminary. He has been associated with the Institute of Paper Chemistry since its inception in 1929. In the last war he was with the 38th Air Squadron, U. S. Army. He holds an honorary LL.D. from Centenary College.

Earl P. Stevenson, President of Arthur D. Little, Inc., of Cambridge, Mass.: He has been an industrial research consultant since 1919. From 1916 to 1918 he was an instructor in chemistry at Massachusetts Institute of Technology. He served with the Chemical Warfare Service in World War I, and with the National Defense Research Committee in the present war. He is Vice President of the New England Industrial Research Foundation, Inc.

II

Table of Contents

Clyde E. Williams, Director of the Battelle Memorial Institute of Columbus, Ohio: He has been active in the chemical and metallurgical field for twenty-seven years. Formerly with the U. S. Bureau of Mines, Hooker Electrochemical Company and Columbia Steel Corporation, he has been associated with the Battelle Memorial Institute since 1929, its Director since 1934. He is Chairman of the War Metallurgy Committee of the National Academy of Sciences, Chairman of the Advisory Committee on Metals and Minerals, War Production Board, and Chief of the Metallurgy Division of the National Defense Research Committee.

A. C. Fieldner, Chief of the Fuels and Explosives Branch of the U. S. Bureau of Mines : He has been associated with the Bureau since 1909 at the Pittsburgh Experimental Station and at Washington, D. C. During World War I his activities included explosives investigations and gas mask research for the Chemical Warfare Service. He had charge of ventilation studies for the Hudson River Tunnel in New York and is the author of numerous monographs and technical articles. Received the Sullivant Medal in 1940.

PART THREE

THEME: "What place should industrial research and development organizations allocate to future work directed primarily toward national security?

The Honorable Robert P. Patterson, Under Secretary of War : He has been in public service since July, 1940, when he became Assistant Secretary of War. A graduate of Harvard Law School, he was admitted to the New York bar in 1915 and was appointed judge of the U. S. District Court, Southern N. Y. District, in 1930, and judge of the U. S. Circuit Court of Appeals in 1939. A major in the first World War, he was awarded the Distinguished Service Cross for extraordinary heroism in action.

Table of Contents

DISCUSSION

Table of Contents

POSTSCRIPT

PART ONE

THEME

"What should be the guiding principles and objectives for the commercial programs of industrial research and development organizations?"

Frank A. Howard

INTRODUCTION
AND SUMMARY

*"There is a great new voice in the world today,
the voice of science and technology."* [1]

Industrial research is now accepted as the main reconnaissance staff of industry. It must keep years ahead of the forces of production, and these forces are headed not only toward a victorious ending of the war, but toward an unprecedented standard of living for the post-war world. Adequate plans must be made for the post-war research which is to lead industry toward its goals. Standard Oil Development Company therefore made its own Silver Anniversary, in October of 1944, the occasion for a Forum on the Future of Industrial Research.

The successful handling of this new force has presented new and difficult problems. Dr. Westbrook Steele reminded the Forum that:

"The cooperation of individual competing companies within an industry, the pooling of their research resources and of their production information during World War I, gave individual industries an unbelievable impetus; new markets, and new products, even new industries evolved. The example of research accomplishments attendant to the prosecution of World War I led to a condition that might well be classified as research worship rather than an understanding of research." [2]

Footnotes in the Introduction and Summary appear at the end of each section.

Introduction and Summary

It was quite natural that this "understanding of research," so badly needed at the end of the first World War, was arrived at first by the great industrial units. They had the best assurance of being able to utilize at a profit in their own business any kind of practical results which came out of the research, and they were able to live through a great many mistakes and acquire their understanding of research by experience. Industrial Research at the beginning of the second World War was still, primarily, the field of activity of "Big Business," and its main function was to apply science to the operations of the great manufacturing and processing industries.

The effect of the war was to draft industrial research for the service of the nation into two new channels, first to advance military and naval science in all directions, and second, to give emergency aid to that tremendous segment of the productive economy which is covered by the term "Small Business." Other forces were also at work to create in all Americans an increasing awareness of their mutual dependence and of their social and national responsibilities.

These considerations led to the conclusion that there were really three main divisions of the "Future of Industrial Research": first, questions which are of general interest, or which concern mainly the highly organized research departments of "Big Business"; second, special problems which "Small Business" faces when it approaches the subject of industrial research; and third, the national security aspect of research planning. The Forum was therefore arranged in three sessions, one devoted to each general division of the subject—the procedure being patterned after that of professional society meetings. The proceedings were all recorded stenographically and are reproduced in this volume.

The writer, who acted as general chairman of the Forum, has made an effort to review the proceedings, by collecting, under question headings, excerpts and summaries of representative views on the principal lines of the discussions. This micro-section of current thinking on the future of industrial research is far from complete, but is a faithful picture so far as it goes, and is compact enough so that the outlines of the whole discussion can be surveyed at once. Reference is made under each heading to pages of the record which seem to bear on that aspect of the discussions.

[1]Robert P. Patterson, page 141.   [2]Steele, pages 90-91.

What is scientific research?

The basis of the scientific process is the reproducible experiment. It is the only fundamental tool at our command for extending our knowledge of the universe. It is the accepted scientific method, and when applied to obtain a better understanding of our environment, it is called "scientific research." Even logic is secondary in importance to the reproducible experiment. Mathematics is the only branch of science which has passed from the realm of the experimental to the utopia of pure logic.[1]

What is fundamental research today is applied research tomorrow. I believe in the end it will always turn out that way.[2]

We have to get a common language. We are getting into the Tower of Babel in technological language and we need to get down to common words.[3]

[1]Midgley, pages 31-32.   [2]Lammot du Pont, page 65.   [3]Kettering, page 68.
See also pages 22, 55-57, 81, 85, 141-142.

What is industrial research?

New industries, and the advancement of old industries, depend first of all on increase in the sum of human knowledge—

and that, of course, is the function of scientific research. But they depend even more on the new application of existing knowledge—and that is development. The amount of scientific knowledge already available which ought to be applied to an industry, and has not yet been applied, is almost always far greater than the new contributions to human knowledge which any industrial research organization can hope to make. Quantitatively, therefore, industrial research work is mainly development work and it is now common to refer to it as "research and development."

The third component of industrial research is the unpredictable one, invention. By invention, new concepts seem to appear suddenly on the earth, or, more commonly, new applications of existing knowledge seem to spring into existence. But the record shows that in an environment of organized research and development effort, the inventive mind reaches a level of productiveness beyond all past experience.

These three—scientific research, development and invention—are the components of technical progress in industry. It is the function of industrial research to harness the three components in a sustained common effort, and to keep the effort headed in the right direction.[1]

[1] Howard, pages 76-77. See also pages 30-33, 41, 55-57, 65-66, 141-143.

What is the objective of industrial research?

In general, the objective of industrial research is the material objective of civilization itself—to prolong life, to improve health and comfort, to enhance happiness, and to enlarge productive ability and usefulness.[1]

The primary responsibility of a research and development organization to the industry with which it is associated is, of course, in the new or improved things which it brings to that industry. Increasingly the choice of what research organizations undertake to do—and their capacity for doing them efficiently—are coming to dictate much of industrial policy. Wise management will see to it that those who direct its research and development organization are an integral part of its policy-making group. Such participation imposes a grave responsibility on the directors of research and development. They must be more than able scientists and technologists—they must be statesmen capable of viewing the problems and accomplishments of the laboratory not only as scientific achievements but as part of an economic and social structure.[2]

[1]Derby, pages 55-57. [2]Jewett, pages 22-23. See also pages 30-35, 46, 68, 74, 81-89, 153-156.

How does research fit into the economy of the profit system?

Because the methods which science uses, both fundamental and applied, are so powerful and certain in achieving the ends sought, money spent through well-organized research and development departments is the least risky and potentially the most profitable of all the expenditures in which industry ventures capital.[1]

The longer a company has been carrying on an extensive research program, the richer that company is. This wealth does not appear on the balance sheet. It manifests itself each time a new demand is made on the company. It also appears as a social factor, because all the members of the group feel that they share a common wealth of knowledge. No matter how thoroughly and promptly the results of this scientific work have been published, there remains a somewhat intangible body of material which cannot be published, but which the group draws on constantly in its new production efforts.[2]

The small business that incorporates its own research department is adaptable, mobile, socially integrated, and profitable.[3]

[1] Jewett, page 22. [2] Land, page 84. [3] Land, page 85. See also pages 18-25, 55-59, 65-67, 99-101, 125-126, 132-135.

How fast has the industrial research effort of the nation grown?

During the past twenty-five years industrial research has expanded ten times. In 1940, 70,000 scientists were engaged in it, and this is a rather large percentage of the total number available. Another sizeable group must remain in educational work, or the whole system will collapse.[1]

As of 1940, expenditures for industrial research and development were at the rate of $300,000,000 per year.[2]

During the war industrial research and what might be called "war research" coalesced so far that it is impossible to separate them for any statistical purpose, but it is clear that when industrial research is separated from war research at the end of the war, the level of expenditures for industrial research itself will be found to be far above the 1940 level.[3]

[1] Midgley, pages 41-42. [2] Derby, page 59. [3] Furer, pages 156-158. See also pages 57-58, 82, 94, 99, 103, 109, 113-114, 135.

What growth is to be expected in the future?

There is no scintilla of evidence at the present time that the forward trend of the past few decades in both fundamental and applied science is likely to slacken in the near future. Quite the contrary. It is still true that each new advance opens up still other opportunities for exploration and advance. The war has slowed down the tempo of production of new knowledge, and in many sectors speeded up the utilization of it, but so far as concerns fundamental science, this is clearly a temporary situation.

Industrial research organizations seem certain, therefore, to grow in number, in size and in diversity of fields covered, and to play an increasingly dominant part in determining our economic, and so, political future.[1]

It is difficult to visualize any further sizeable expansion until our supply of scientifically trained personnel can be increased through the normal process of education. This will require at least a few years after the war ends.[2]

An entirely new trend in corporate organization is appearing in modern small companies. In this new kind of company the scientist is not an adjunct to a routine manufacturing organization. Instead, the company is organized around the concept of continuous development of new and better products, deriving day by day from the activity of its pure scientists, applied scientists, engineers and sales development men. This new company is resourceful, adaptable, and mobile. The morale is high throughout. Everyone senses the continuous progress, and the research attitude permeates every member of the organization.[3]

[1] Jewett, page 18. [2] Midgley, page 42. [3] Land, pages 81-85. See also pages 38-41, 49-52, 62-63, 90-96, 152.

How is industrial research work organized?

The past twenty-five years have established certain concepts of research organization that may be expected to endure for some time to come. The research "team," as a unit in this organization, has gained popularity. The individuals of any particular team are chosen for their qualifications in their field of specialization, as it is related to the problem to be studied. This is a different approach to organization than the conception of a departmental head, with a variety of assistants. Both types of organization have their places. The team is better adapted to the solution of problems involving two or more fields of science, while the conventional organization works best on problems substantially confined to a single field. It has been observed that the problems involving multiple fields are becoming more numerous and hence the "team conception" is gaining in practice.[1]

The team organization is greatly superior to any scheme of farming out portions of the problem to individual laboratories. This is true because at all stages of the work the several elements react on one another; and what can or cannot be done in one field determines what can or cannot be done in another.[2]

No director who is any good ever really "directs" any research. What he does is to protect the research men from the people who want to "direct" them.[3]

[1]Midgley, page 42. [2]Jewett, pages 18-19. [3]Mees, page 48. See also pages 23, 43, 66, 125-126, 134-135, 165-166.

Where should an industrial research laboratory be located?

A problem that eternally plagues management is location. There is no ideal location. There are advantages in being near the production center, there are advantages in being away from it. But I know of no advantage in complete isolation.

With isolation comes inadequacy of social contacts between the professional employees and others engaged in similar activities. The result is deadening to the whole organization.

Introduction and Summary

There are undeniable advantages in having the laboratory personnel well informed with respect to production problems and economies. This can best be obtained by proximity. On the other hand, proximity of the research laboratory to production is an ever-present temptation to the production management to draw the laboratory into undertaking or studying the daily bread-and-butter problems which the production unit should be capable of solving for itself.

Possibly the solution for maximum results can be obtained by having two laboratories, one at the plant and another a few hundred miles distant. Ultimately, the problems each is best adapted to solve will find their proper atmosphere.[1]

[1] Midgley, pages 43-44. See also page 82.

What are the main problems in research by small business?

The thing that could best be contributed by the research people of this country to small business would be some form of educational program—not preaching to management, but interesting management in the habit of mind of research men.[1]

There is already a widespread and intelligent interest in research by business executives in small companies. More funds are available than are being spent. Opportunities for research and development are recognized and the missing element is in technical and scientific manpower.[2]

Cooperative research by small business has been extraordinarily successful and has a large and important future ahead of it. When it comes to competitive research, a full solution has not yet been found.[3]

Institutions like the Mellon Institute, the Battelle Memorial Institute, the Southern Research Institute which is now in process of formation, or, in limited sectors, organizations like Arthur D. Little, Inc., can provide the values of a complete research organization on a reasonable fee basis.[4]

The specific step which will most aid small business in the use of research in the immediate future is the employment of men who speak the research man's language—men trained in our great technical educational institutions. It is not sufficient for the business executive to be sympathetic toward research; he must also have an understanding of its techniques, and the ability to select the right kind of men. The services of a research consultant, and of related agencies, are seriously handicapped if the client does not have on his own staff at least one individual competent to participate in the work and see that the findings are intelligently and usefully applied. It is becoming increasingly necessary for the small company to support a technical staff and it is from these expenditures that it may expect to receive the highest return.[5]

[1]Morehead Patterson, page 125. [2]Stevenson, page 101. [3]Lewis, page 136. [4]Jewett, page 20. [5]Stevenson, pages 102, 99-100. See also pages 90 ff., 101 ff., 125-126, 132, 136-137.

What is the field for cooperative research programs by entire industries?

Greater progress for the industry as a whole and therefore for its components lies in a collective attack upon the problems of fundamental science which lie at the root of most production and development problems.[1]

An important, if not the most important, obstacle to the development of cooperative research institutions is the inhibitive effect of our federal statutory prohibitions, which hang like the sword of Damocles over the head of cooperative undertakings of this character. Unless we are willing to face this problem realistically, not only will we continue to stifle new enterprise, but we will hazard our world position as an industrial nation.[2]

[1]Steele, page 88. [2]Willard, pages 127-128. See also pages 18-19, 42.

What is the place of the universities in industrial research?

There is only one way in which men can be trained for the research phases of industry. After they have received their broad technical training, they must be taught the research technique by being given research to do, and in the early phases of that training, that research work can be done in the university to the best advantage. In the conduct of that research, results are sure to accrue. And that is the field which the university should occupy in the conduct of industrial research. Progress has already been made. Large numbers of great institutions have successfully undertaken work in that field.[1]

[1]Lewis, pages 136-137. See also pages 68-69.

What policies of government and business handicap the training of men for future research?

It is decidedly relevant to consider carefully the sole source of supply of new scientists—the universities. The universities at the present time are in a tragic state. The policy of the U. S. Government and War Department is to eliminate completely during the war period the normal training of men qualified to specialize in science, who are physically able to become soldiers. The U. S. Government's attitude with respect to the training of chemists is in pointed contrast to that of England,

Russia and France—and, it is reported, even Germany. For in these other countries highly qualified youths have been selected to receive regular training in science during the war period.

Four instances are cited in which men in university chemistry departments between thirty and forty years of age, with most promising futures in pure science, have been offered industrial positions at three to five times their university salaries. In the next years, when recovery in personnel in the universities is impossible, there is no better way of crippling the chemistry departments, of reducing them to mediocrity and thus lowering the standard of training of the young technical men of the future than by adopting this policy.[1]

[1] Adams, pages 50-51. See also page 36.

What is the relation of patents to the future of industrial research?

Historically, a patent is a governmental grant to the inventor of an absolute monopoly over his invention for a limited period, for the purpose of fostering new industries.[1]

Under the influence of the patent system modern industry has come into existence. The steam engine was developed by James Watt bcause he knew he could get a patent monopoly on the results and sell steam engines at a profit. The future of industrial research is intimately bound up with the future of our patent system. There will be attacks made on it in the future as there have been in the past, probably by individuals who have little knowledge of their subject. It would seem that a comprehensive discussion of the exact situation at the time would be all that is needed to retain the merits of our present system.[2]

We know that for every patent which creates a new industry, there are many patents which do nothing but advance an old industry. When you try to apply to a patent on the advancement of an old industry, the simple concept of absolute monopoly, you are often in difficulty. Industry realizes that, and has been making the patent system work by applying to it the simple rule of "Live and let live." It has been instinctively and consciously adapting the system to changing economic conditions by its licensing policies. There is a borderline zone between the field in which sound economics and current business practice justify the maintenance of a complete monopoly, and the field in which they call for unrestricted licensing. Industry on the one hand and those responsible for the enforcement of the anti-trust laws on the other, have each displayed a little lack of understanding in their handling of the problems in this borderline zone, and this friction discourages research.

There is one other patent problem. Just now too many courts do not like patents, and do not often sustain them. Experience shows that this is likely to be a temporary phase. There is nothing very fundamental about it, although the Patent Planning Commission recommends legislation to correct some of the heresies that have crept into judicial reasoning on the validity of patents.[3]

[1]Howard, page 137.   [2]Midgley, pages 32, 33, 38.   [3]Howard, pages 137-138. See also pages 36-39, 59-60, 129, 133-134.

What about government in research?

From the earliest days of national history the government of the United States has conducted scientific investigations in order to establish a sound basis for its legislative and administrative activities. Governmental agencies were pioneers in this country in carrying on research. As the population has increased and new problems have arisen, such as those relating to agriculture, conservation of natural resources and general economic conditions, the government has found it necessary to extend greatly the scope of its research program. It is now engaged in research on a vast scale. As a matter of fact, there are about 125 different units of the government that are engaged in research.[1]

Those great federal research institutions which have served us so well in the past years and are serving us so well today have been a breeding ground for scientific men.[2]

The great objection to delegating to political government control of much of industrial research and development is inherent in the structure of government itself. Government is necessarily political, *i.e.*, motivated by the resultant of many forces, which must often be compromised if anything is to be accomplished.[3]

There are certain types of research which must be carried on with government financing and government help. But it should stop with those things which are purely for war or national defense, and let the private initiative and business competitive system carry as much of the load as possible.[4]

[1]Fieldner, pages 113-114. [2]Willard, page 128. [3]Jewett, page 21. [4]Dewey, page 75. See also pages 25, 60-61, 64, 144-145, 147 ff., 160-168.

How is industrial research related to national security?

Our troops have been equipped with weapons, equalling or surpassing those of the enemy; final victory has been brought immeasurably closer, as a result of the efforts of our scientists and technicians.[1]

Introduction and Summary

The last four years have demonstrated that the civilian scientist can contribute in an outstanding way to the invention, development and operation of all manner of instrumentalities of war.[2]

Peace is going to come to us again, and we hope also that it will endure for a long time; but those of us who are in positions of social responsibility, in industry or in government, must remember that peace is largely a state of mind of a victorious people.[3]

In the next world war, which will inevitably come some day, but we hope not in our lifetime, the "lightning war" will be much more feasible because of the rapid development that is taking place, that cannot be stopped, and that will be world wide. The only safeguard against it by a free and peaceful people, such as ourselves, is to be so far ahead in our progress that no nation will take the risk of attacking us.[4]

[1]Robert P. Patterson, page 146.   [2]Furer, page 156.   [3]Gillmor, page 154.
[4]Gillmor, page 155. See also pages 160-168, 170-171.

What are the problems in the continuing application of industrial research to national security?

Research and development devoted to the weapons, tools and techniques of war will not go on to the extent required for our national security unless support, guidance, even control, emanate from central mechanisms. When peace comes we shall have the greatest difficulty in keeping even a small portion of our best scientific brains on the job of maintaining the weapons of our armed forces at the high peak of effectiveness they now occupy.

The first question is how we shall obtain for the Federal Government the full-time or consulting services of scientists on the highest level. An important obstacle in enlisting the aid of industry is the difficulty of liaison and interchange between the military services and industry.

How shall extensive work in weapon development be financed? Financing by way of subsidy or contract payments will often not be enough. We shall need other forms of incentive, financial in character or otherwise.

In my judgment a single unified defense agency, combining the Army and Navy, would go far towards solving many of the problems to which I have referred.

I know of no group as well qualified to answer the questions I have raised as this group. I know of no group which will devote itself to that task with more energy, high purpose and sincerity.[1]

After this discussion we can all of us see that in the peacetime years to come it is absolutely essential that we in industrial research and development set aside a part—and by a part I mean an appreciable part—of our endeavors, and that means organization, that means the men, that means the facilities, and it probably also means the money, that will be required to see that this country is kept at least abreast, and if we do our job properly, kept out ahead as regards munitions and weapons of war.[2]

[1]Robert P. Patterson, pages 145, 146, 148-153. [2]Russell, page 171. See also pages 155-168.

Frank B. Jewett

THE FUTURE OF
INDUSTRIAL RESEARCH
THE VIEW OF A PHYSICIST

IN ORDER TO APPRAISE the value of a physicist's point of view in connection with "probable future responsibilities of industrial research and development organizations" it is essential to know the present and prospective contributions of physics and physicists to the accomplishments of such organizations.

Modern physics in an industrial organization in the hands of skilled imaginative physicists, *i.e.*, men trained in the ways of matter and of the forces which influence it, is analogous to mechanical engineering in the field of engineering technology. Just as no substantial progress can be made in any field of engineering without the aid of trained mechanical engineers, so no substantial progress can be made in an industrial research organization without recourse to physics and highly trained, skilled physicists.

The extent to which such recourse must be had will vary with the field of interest of the organization. It will be dominant in a laboratory like Bell Telephone Laboratories and may be minor in a chemical or biological industry, but it cannot be escaped if full value is to be obtained from one of the other sciences.

In the industrial field the place of chemistry and physics and of men widely trained in them has become firmly established during the past two or three decades. No applied science industry can now be secure or hope to grow without them. This is because exact knowledge of the fundamental sciences and of the methods by which it is derived provides the holders of it with powerful facile tools with which to fashion new things of utility.

Organizations properly equipped with such men and the tools they require are in position to create entirely new industries, to modify old ones to meet changing conditions, or rapidly to adapt newly acquired knowledge derived from fundamental science research. There is no scintilla of evidence at the present time that the forward trend of the past few decades in both fundamental and applied science is likely to slacken in the near future—quite the contrary. It is still true that each new advance opens up still other opportunities for exploration and advance. The war has slowed down the tempo of production of new knowledge and in many sectors speeded up the utilization of it, but so far as concerns fundamental science this is clearly a temporary situation.

Industrial research organizations seem certain therefore to grow both in number, in size and in diversity of fields covered, and to play an increasingly dominant part in determining our economic and so our political future.

They do not need to be large to be efficient, and in a host of industries concerned with specialized products we will find small laboratories doing distinguished creative work. In many fields, however, the products will be such as to involve a wide range of physical, chemical and biological problems so interwoven as to call for scientific attack from many angles, and so we will have large research organizations with specialists and specialized facilities in many fields, all organized to function as a coordinated team.

Experience has shown that this is the most powerful, effective and economical method of handling complex problems. It is greatly superior to any scheme of farming out portions of the problem to individual laboratories. This results from the fact that at all stages of the work the several elements react on one another and that what can or cannot be done in one field determines what can or cannot be done in another. Facility for intimate daily intercourse between the research and development expedites progress, eliminates much false work and insures a better end-product.

By this I do not mean to imply that there is no place for specialized industrial research laboratories nor that great research organizations will not find it profitable to seek their assistance. In general I think, however, that such assistance will be confined to questions which are in themselves essentially complete problems.

Experience with such large, well organized groups, properly integrated into the other parts of the industry, has indicated also that whatever the organization chart may show on paper there are in fact no sharp lines of demarcation between the several functions of the business. From the groups which are involved in what is essentially fundamental science research to those engaged in development, engineering, manufacturing and operation, the transitions are lapweld joints over which information flows smoothly in both directions.

Nor does the desirability of such comprehensive research and development organizations predicate inevitably only great consolidated industries. Some industries are of such a character that maximum values to the public can only be obtained by having one, or at most, a few large units. In such cases great research organizations covering a wide diversity of fields of science and serving but one single unit can be justified.

In other fields there can be many units which compete with each other but which have a common interest in advancing the base of scientific and technical information on which all are dependent for success. For such industries one or more large complete cooperative research and development organizations can serve to give to all the participants information and assistance, which each can then adapt to its own particular needs or ingenuity, but which the units severally could not afford to acquire separately.

For still other situations, where the industrial units are small or widely diversified, institutions like the Mellon Institute, the Battelle Memorial Institute, the Southern Research Institute which is now in process of formation, or, in limited sectors, organizations like Arthur D. Little, Inc., can provide the values of a complete research organization on a reasonable fee basis.

All of these types of organizations are parts, essentially, of a free economy system where initiation and operation are wholly in the hands of private management. So far as one or another of these schemes—variants of them or others which may be devised—can be employed, I personally am strongly convinced that they are the preferred methods for insuring maximum benefit not only to industry but to the nation as well.

There are, however, very large sectors concerned with applied science where for one reason or another it is difficult to see how the maximum benefits of scientific knowledge can be made available to the nation without active participation of political government, be it state or national.

Most outstanding examples of these fields are things like agriculture and public health, where the number to be benefited is very great, the units are small and uncoordinated, and the difficulties of voluntary cooperation correspondingly large. In these sectors there seems to be no escape from large governmental participation as the only effective means of providing the funds and facilities which the nature and magnitude of the scientific and technical problems demand.

Intrusion of the Political

The great objection to delegating to political government control of much of industrial research and development is inherent in the structure of government itself. Government is necessarily political, *i.e.*, motivated by the resultant of many forces which must often be compromised if anything is to be accomplished. In such circumstances it is difficult, if not impossible, to insure against the intrusion of political factors which are inimical to the full realization of all that fundamental and applied science is capable of doing. In addition to this, government must necessarily be controlled, if it is to operate at all effectively, by general and rather rigid rules many of which we are commonly wont to describe as "red tape" and which must be applied impartially over a wide variety of activities.

Thus, quite aside from the pernicious intrusion of political factors which have no place in a research undertaking, the setting is one in which a large number of the best of our scientific and technical men are reluctant to operate. As a result, there is a large tendency toward the expenditure of huge sums of money for what is essentially second-rate work done by those less-than-best men who are content to spend their lives as poorly compensated civil servants. In saying this I do not want to be misunderstood as implying that there are not a large number of A-1 scientists in government laboratories. Some of our finest scientific work comes out of them.

During the last few years there has been a large amount of talk, discussion and agitation about making the fruits of scientific research and development work more generally available to the public through an enlarged intrusion of government into what we have been accustomed to consider the province of the individual or of industry.

When boiled down, much of this discussion is found to be based either on misconceptions, on real reasons that are masked, or on a desire to get something for nothing or something at the public's expense. If the ultimate object of all that we are trying to do by way of industrial research is to get into the hands of the greatest number of people the maximum benefits of applied science, much of that which is being agitated for, if realized, will tend to defeat that objective by so dissipating the forces needed to create the required production that it cannot be attained.

All productive science, both fundamental and applied, is essentially creative. It is the result of the operation of men's minds, and it flowers most profusely in an atmosphere of maximum freedom. No man or group of men can predict in advance what will come out of other men's minds. Nor can they constrain men to produce new ideas. The most that they can do is to provide a favorable environment for creative effort and, if necessary, later impose controls on the use of those creations to the end that they will be employed for the benefit, and not the detriment, of society.

Because the methods which science uses, both fundamental and applied, are so powerful and certain in achieving the ends sought, money spent through well organized research and development departments is the least risky and potentially the most profitable of all the expenditures in which industry ventures capital.

The primary responsibility of a research and development organization to the industry with which it is associated is, of course, in the new or improved things which it brings to that industry. Increasingly the choice of what research organizations undertake to do—and their capacity for doing them efficiently—are coming to dictate much of industrial policy. Wise management will see to it that those who direct its research and development organization are an integral part of its policy-making group.

Such participation imposes a grave responsibility on the directors of research and development. They must be more than able scientists and technologists—they must be industrial statesmen capable of viewing the problems and accomplishments of the laboratory not only as scientific achievements but as part of an economic and social structure. They must be capable of discarding work—no matter how interesting technically—whenever it is clear that it does not fit into that structure. On the other hand, they must be prepared to support to the limit those undertakings which they are convinced *do* fit into the economic and social structure, even though their less informed associates in management think otherwise.

In conclusion I should like to raise a warning flag. There is such impetus to the idea of enlarged industrial research at the moment and so much of value which might be accomplished that we are in imminent danger of building organizations which we have not the trained men to staff. A research laboratory without good men in it can be a serious liability.

Discussion: GEORGE W. LEWIS

Dr. Jewett has presented an excellent paper covering his years of experience as a leader in the field of industrial research.

Dr. Jewett in his paper pointed out the many disadvantages of research controlled by government. The organization I represent, the NACA (National Advisory Committee for Aeronautics), has had some measure of success in the field of aeronautical research over a period of twenty-five years. The NACA is one of the oldest industrial research organizations in the government, having been established in 1915, and is controlled by fifteen members appointed by the President. The NACA is an independent government organization, and

I attribute its success in part to the independence and in part to the close cooperation with industry and with other government organizations.

The engineering science of aeronautics was indeed very young when the committee was established in 1915, but since that time we have been struggling with physical problems. One of the first problems was to evaluate the results of wind-tunnel tests. Small models, say of 1/20 scale, tested in a wind tunnel with a speed of forty miles an hour, gave results that in many cases proved very inaccurate. The difference between the results obtained on the very small model in the wind tunnel and the results obtained in flight was due to the Reynolds-number effect. To correct our wind-tunnel results it was necessary to design and construct a wind tunnel that would give the same Reynolds number as resulted from flight tests. This meant the construction of a wind tunnel in a large steel chamber, capable of operating under pressure of 300 pounds per square inch or 20 atmospheres. This wind tunnel gave results on models and wings that could be used with confidence in the design of airplanes. An expensive piece of equipment of this kind could not be constructed by any single member of the industry, but the government could properly provide this equipment for the benefit of the entire industry.

Another physical problem that has held back the advance of aviation—and Chairman Kettering is most responsible for alleviating this particular shortcoming of our aviation fuels—is the problem of detonation. The government is definitely concerned. Detonation limits the performance of our aircraft. We have tried to find out what detonation is. We have built high-speed cameras, taken photographs at the rate of 40,000, even 100,000, frames per second through a glass window in an engine cylinder head. So far we have been unable to discover exactly what happens. It is still a major problem.

Aeronautical Problems

Another physical problem which is very pertinent at the moment is the problem of compressibility effects. Whenever the airspeed over any part of the airplane reaches the velocity of sound, which is approximately 750 miles per hour, a compression shock is formed which greatly increases the drag or resistance of the airplane, and greatly increases the instability. To study this problem the committee has constructed 500- and 600-mile-an-hour wind tunnels, which could not be constructed by any member of the industry, and the results of the studies are made known and benefit the entire industry. This problem is the present stumbling block in increasing our airplane speeds much above 500 miles an hour.

I have mentioned only three problems of such character that only the government could best provide the special equipment necessary for the general good of the industry. I recognize that research in aviation is a special case of industrial research in which the government can be most effective and helpful to an industry. Research in government, as Dr. Jewett has pointed out, is most valuable when it affects great numbers. In our particular case, the National Advisory Committee for Aeronautics has had the problem of providing, to a new and growing industry, fundamental data that will permit the design of the best military and commercial airplanes.

Discussion: LYMAN J. BRIGGS

I am inclined to the opinion that the field of greatest usefulness for the Bureau of Standards lies (1) in providing better standards and methods of measurement; (2) in helping to extend the frontiers of knowledge through basic research; and (3) in helping to make available to industry the vast fund of information that already exists. I think that industrial research, as its name implies, is primarily a job for industry itself.

The bureau is fortunate in having men on its visiting committee who are closely identified with industrial research. Dr. Jewett is a member of this committee and Chairman Kettering is a former member. Any suggestions as to ways in which our work may be made more effective and helpful will be gratefully received.

Discussion: CHAIRMAN C. F. KETTERING

I am sure that when we think of the subject of physics in engineering very broadly, we always find difficulty, as Dr. Jewett said, in the lapweld. I think it was Dr. Urey who, when asked, "What is the difference between pure science and industrial research?" made the statement that the difference was twenty years. I think that seems to be about right.

You must understand that many of the statements which Dr. Jewett has made are from a man who has complete control of the planning, of the engineering development, and of everything else in his operation; but in miscellaneous industries, such as some of us come from, I should say that there are "interrupted lapwelds" in a good many cases, and not a smooth flow.

I think the great problem that comes up in the subject of all industrial research is how to "package" it; that is, how much can you put in a package and pass on through production without completely disrupting the industry.

So it seems to me that out of this group could come a committee that would set up what we know for sure and what we don't know at all, only by synonyms. So much of our information is simply knowing another word for the same thing.

Some of us in industrial research have been working to try to outline a system whereby we could separate, as Dr. Lewis has said, this question of detonation. One of the problems we had there was to find out what part belonged to the engine and what part belonged to the fuel. The commercial men in both lines refused to allow us to tag any of it on either one of them, so it all belonged to the other one.

Sometimes, because you can't allocate the thing specifically, you do get into this difficulty of knowing where to put the research. There are those general problems such as in aeronautics, involving, for example, full size scale wind tunnels, that have to be done entirely by government organizations.

The thing we have tried to work on in our group for a great many years is to find out the procedure by which we can analyze out of any system the preliminary problems and find out where they belong. Sometimes an engine designer will start to work on an engine problem that has nothing to do with the engine at all, but before he gets through it is a metallurgical problem; and when you get into the metallurgical department you find its handling depends on what the head of some production organization will allow his organization to do. That becomes psychology, and so far as I know, physicists have not been too good psychologists.

Discussion: FRANK B. JEWETT

The statements by George Lewis and Dr. Briggs are not a refutation of what I had in mind but a complete exemplification of it.

The Bureau of Standards, of course, needs no justification from anybody. Its record is almost beyond reproach, and it serves everybody; so, since it *does* serve everybody it is an ideal type of thing to have under the kind of control that it is under, and to have as its job that which we all need: the certification of the standards without which we can't make any great progress.

With regard to the National Advisory Committee for Aeronautics, I think it is an almost perfect exemplification of a proper cooperation between government and industry. It was wisely set up, and it has been wisely administered through the years, essentially under civilian, non-governmental control through its board of directors. It is frequently used as the typical example of what government could do if it moved farther into the whole industrial research field.

There are two or three of us participating in the Forum—Admiral Furer is one—who have recently been engaged in the work of a committee organized by the Secretaries of War and Navy to advise them with regard to the organization of postwar military research of the type which can best be done in civilian agencies.

In the course of that discussion, it was inevitable that the NACA should be brought out as a type of thing which would simply set the pace for a wide variety of government participation—active participation—and control of industrial research.

The discussion of the place of government in industrial research is not over by any means, and there will be a great deal more of it before the present excitement is over. I should just like to express my own views which I outlined at the time of these committee meetings—my analysis of why the NACA has been so tremendously successful during these past twenty-five years.

When World War I ended, there had been, as you all remember, the beginnings of the incursion of the airplane into both civil and military life, and it was sensed by everybody who gave thought to it, and who knew something about physics and science in general, that it had great possibilities. But it was equally recognized that to achieve any objective, whether military or civil, was going to require the expenditure of such huge sums of money ventured in the experimental stages that in the uncertainties of the future it was difficult to see how civilian industry alone and unaided could do the job. And military requirements of necessity had to follow civilian requirements.

There was, therefore, even during the period of the battleship-sinking era of the twenties, a realization that military money could and should be spent in this particular field, and the combination of requirements, both civil and military, made it possible to get money from government funds to be administered partly for military purposes.

In trying to look forward into the future it is difficult, for me at any rate, to see any problems at the moment which are comparable in their fundamental characteristics to the one which was solved twenty-five years ago by the setting up of the NACA.

So it seems to me that in connection with our future discussions of the place of government in industrial research, it is wise to go back to some of the fundamentals and see to what extent and in what direction the marriage of government activity and private activity can profitably be made to the benefit of all concerned.

Thomas Midgley, Jr.

THE FUTURE OF
INDUSTRIAL RESEARCH
THE VIEW OF A CHEMIST

SOME TWENTY-FIVE or thirty thousand years ago a new species of animal appeared on this earth. There is nothing remarkable about new species appearing from time to time. The history of the ages is filled with such events; but this particular species differed in one characteristic from all that had preceded it. Instead of adapting itself to the various environments thrust upon it by an unfriendly and ever-changing world it had an instinct to adapt its environment to suit itself. Indeed this was the most remarkable characteristic it possessed. It began by exterminating all of its potential competitors within the genus homo, leaving only itself as the representative of that group. Recently it has given itself the species designation of sapiens. Homo sapiens, or in other words, ourselves, began the readjustment of its environment by doing the obvious. It cleared land for agriculture, built houses for protection against the weather and various enemies, including itself, and, to a limited extent, destroyed those animals antagonistic to it as best it could. It made into vassal creatures dogs, cattle, chickens and pigs and changed the nature of many wild plants to make easier its labor of providing itself with food. Yet there remained many parts of its environment over which it could exert no control; for example, lightning, hurricanes, earthquakes and floods. This lack of control puzzled it. Instinct urged it on and somewhere in its subconscious mental processes mankind felt that a better understanding of that universe, which it knew to be its own, might aid it in its eternal fight to control that universe. At first imagination was given full sway. Superior creatures to itself were conceived, which it assumed had control of many things. Sacrificial offerings and prayers were invented to obtain the friendship of these superiors; but gradually, through the past two thousand years, such childish superstition has been replaced by what we call the scientific process.

What is this scientific process? Indeed, all too often the term is used to glamorize simple common sense, and then again it is used by charlatans to give respectability to what otherwise obviously would be in conflict with common sense. A better definition is desirable. To my mind the basis of the scientific process is the reproducible experiment.

Facts are still, and probably always will be, determined by vote, quite as the College of Cardinals determined the number of feathers in the Archangels' wings just a few centuries ago. To the modern scientifically trained mind this process seems somewhat ridiculous; but was it? The number had to be determined for the benefit of painters, sculptors and architects and how else could it have been done? Indeed, the same process is in use today when groups of scientists gather to hear discussions of controversial subjects. There are, however, two points of basic difference. Whereas the number of feathers was decided by majority vote, in science we require a practically unanimous vote for establishing a fact. The second point is the type of evidence required by the voter to influence his decision. Revelations, dreams, supernatural authority are now out, and even logic is of secondary importance to the reproducible experiment.

Mathematics is the only branch of science which claims exemption from this rule. Two thousand years ago, mathematics passed from the realm of the experimental to the utopia of pure logic. It is interesting to note that prior to that time mathematics had been an experimental science. The Egyptians and Babylonians had determined crude values for *pi* by experimentation, and several formulas had likewise been developed. The Greeks, however, who were long on logic and short on experimentation, transformed mathematics into an exact science—the only transformation of its kind ever to have taken place. Is it too much to hope that other sciences, such as chemistry and physics, may some day be similarly transformed? One may always hope, even though fulfillment is still far away.

Permit me to recapitulate. We are the only species of living creatures that even conceives of exerting any control over the environment thrust upon it. Admittedly, this control is far from complete. Its extension is greatly to be desired. To accomplish this extension we need to increase our knowledge of the universe in which we live. The only fundamental tool at our command, for extending this knowledge, is the reproducible experiment. This is the accepted scientific method, and when applied to obtain a better understanding of our environment is designated by such terms as fundamental research or pure science research or academic research. Once new facts about our environment (which is synonymous with our universe where and when we come in contact with it) are discovered, we can make use of these new facts to alter or control our environment to some extent. The process of applying the facts, determined by fundamental research, to a better control of our environment is called applied research or development work or invention.

For some reason, best known to our lawmakers, the discoverers of new facts are denied any special rights to financial benefits that ultimately may result from these discoveries. On the other hand, those who can apply such discoveries to improvements of environment, for their fellow men, are granted the exclusive privilege of exploiting these improvements, for a limited period of time, provided they make public the nature and details of the improvements in documents called patents.

Whether this arrangement is right, fair or just is beside the point. Under its influence modern industry has come into existence and homo sapiens has made great gains in controlling his environment. This, at least, makes it good.

In the early history of modern industry there is little evidence that it either knew or appreciated the fact that the patent system was responsible for its birth. All it knew or cared about was that it had a steam engine to run machines with, that machines could be operated by men hired at low wages to make things that could be sold at a profit. Little did it care that the steam engine had been developed by James Watt because James Watt knew he could get a "patent monopoly" on the results and sell steam engines at a profit. Few of the early units of our "modern industry" gave heed to the fact that they could follow in the footsteps of James Watt and increase their profits by contributing to the inventive and developmental process. Thus it was that, for over a century and a half, the inventor went his lonely way, suffering hardship and sacrifice, often being looked upon as crazy, and finally spending the later years of his life in protecting the rights granted to him by his government. If you think this an exaggeration study the life of Charles Goodyear and then ask yourself if it was worth it, just to stand in the Hall of Fame, where he should be, but isn't.

Inevitably industry finally saw the light. Many of you can recall the "drafting room" of fifty years ago, how it grew into the engineering department which in turn gave birth to the research laboratory.

Industrial research has come into existence by this revolution. The field of industrial research is restricted, primarily, to making use of the discoveries of academic research to improve our control over our environment which then may be used for profit making through the patent process. It must be noted, however, that our knowledge of our environmental universe is far from complete and that it often becomes necessary, in the course of prosecuting industrial research, to deviate from the primary process in order to determine additional facts about the universe so that these facts may be applied. There is no legal process for restricting the use of these facts, once determined. Secrecy and secrecy alone can retain control.

This is not quite as it should be. There might be some mechanism devised whereby the discoverer of new facts could preempt their use for a brief period of time, a period at least long enough for him to determine some of their various applications to environmental control. Thus would be established a motive for industrial research to make public, at once, the discoveries it makes concerning the natural laws. I should like to point out that despite the profit motives to keep secret the discoveries of fact which are continually being made by industrial research, the large majority of industrial operators do make these discoveries public within a reasonable time. Such an attitude of conscious service to society should receive more praise and recognition than it does.

Instead of trying to *aid* industrial research to benefit the society which has created it, it seems inherently human for many people to do their utmost to obstruct it. Possibly the suddenness with which industrial research has developed to its present position of eminence has generated unwarranted fears on the part of many people who scarcely understand it—fears that the power it obviously possesses over our future progress may be abused, fears that a monopoly of brains may be in the making, or just plain fears of change. Whatever the fears may be, I am of the opinion that their basic cause is simply the sudden appearance of industrial research in our economy. Had industrial research developed simultaneously with modern in-

Process of "Catching Up"

dustry over the past one hundred and fifty years instead of merely during the past twenty-five (to a large extent), these fears would be non-existent. That industrial research should have been developing over the one hundred and fifty year period seems obvious to us now; its rapidity of growth during the past twenty-five years has been largely a "catching up" process. Whether or not it has completely caught up with other industrial activities is a question for debate. I am of the opinion that it has not. Assuming that I am right in this opinion there is still a further point for debate. Will it? This is a far more difficult question to answer than the first. It hinges on so many intangible factors, factors which only the future itself will fully develop.

I should like to discuss a few of these factors at random, more for the purpose of disclosing the uncoordinated thinking that is taking place rather than to attempt a solution of any one of them.

For example, there is one school of thought that was rather vociferous some ten years ago, which believed that all industrial research should be ended for some indefinite period, until, as they expressed it, the humanities had caught up. Since the war developed, these theorists have been rather quiescent; but given a period of unemployment, after hostilities cease, it is a practical certainty they will be heard from again. Frankly, the thought processes involved are beyond my poor comprehension. How unemployment may be reduced by increasing it or how stopping industry will start employment is merely a denial of logic to me.

Then there is the thought that placing all industrial research under governmental direction would result in accelerated progress. I have read the various Kilgore Bills and the arguments for and against; but again I must confess that I simply cannot understand the logic involved. Somehow, it seems to me, the proponents of this and similar proposals assume that research scientists are going to work largely for the pleasure of presenting the results of their labors to society free gratis, without any desire for rewards for themselves. There are such men of course. Thank God there are, for without them I don't know how we should ever get the next generation of college students educated. But there are none to spare. It is quite true that scientists, as a group, are more willing to work for the sheer joy of satisfying their inquiring minds than are most other people; but it is also true that scientists have wives who want new automobiles and fur coats, quite as physicians' and lawyers' and judges' wives do, and scientists have children, just as other folks do, and scientists like to feel that they can raise and educate these children, as other folks do, and to do it they are deserving of an opportunity to obtain a financial reward that is somewhat proportional to the services they render society. I have never been able to figure out where they get it under the Kilgore proposal.

There are also those who would change our patent system. Somehow these people have an aversion to the government's granting a monopoly for seventeen years to any individual for making public an invention. These people seem to think the government is giving away something to the inventor. Actually, by its very nature, a patentable invention brings into existence with it a natural monopoly, which merely requires secrecy for its preservation. Obviously, the commercialization of many inventions would destroy the secret; but of others it would not. In either case the inventor could retain his natural monopoly and use it for his own benefits in whatever way he might choose as long as he did not disclose his secret. This is the situation the inventor finds himself in when he goes to the government voluntarily to accept the bargain the government offers him, which simply is this: "Make your invention public and you can *retain* your monopoly for seventeen years." If the government decides to drive a much harder bargain it is permissible to wonder how many inventors will volunteer to surrender their natural monopolies? Certainly those who make an invention which may be exploited and kept secret will scarcely be expected to do so. The results will be disastrous.

Then, too, there are court decisions that are difficult to understand. The Supreme Court declares that Marconi's patents are invalid for lack of invention after they have expired. In another decision it uses the term "Flash of Genius," as though the method of making an invention was of more importance than the invention itself. Another court proclaims that an individual can make an invention; but if a group, working together, perform the same act and obtain the same result it is not an invention. It is all very disconcerting. To my way of thinking, which I have tried to develop in the earlier part of this discussion, any increase of control over our environment, or beneficial alteration thereof, is invention. The method by which such results are obtained is of no importance. The attitude of these courts seems to be comparable to that of a general who decides that if a regiment takes a position from the enemy no advance has been made, whereas if a single individual does so it is a commendable act and deserving of a medal—in the court cases, a patent.

Some few years ago the enemies of our patent system were in the habit of proclaiming that there were great numbers of "suppressed" patents. A "suppressed" patent was supposed to be a patent of value that was not being "worked" because of some selfish motive on the part of the owner, such as having an obsolete plant that he would be forced to scrap if he put the patent to work. This story has many variations. Then these propagandists proposed new laws for forced licensing as a

No Suppressed Patents

corrective measure of this imaginary abuse of our patent system. In the interest of determining the facts I issued an invitation in the News Edition of Industrial and Engineering Chemistry to any and all chemists who might know of such cases, to report them to me anonymously, giving the *serial number* of the patent. I received five replies. Not a single case was justified. There are *no* suppressed patents.

I am not here to discuss the future of our patent system and I feel that I have taken more of your time on this subject than could be justified were it not for the fact that the future of industrial research is so intimately bound up with it. I am proud of our patent system, proud of its past record—a record which speaks for itself—and I sincerely believe that this record alone fully justifies its retention.

There will be attacks made on it in the future, as there have been in the past, probably by individuals who have little knowledge of their subject. It would seem that a comprehensive discussion of the exact situation at the time would be all that is needed to retain the merits of our present system.

Assuming that no disastrous changes are made in our patent system, certain trends in industrial research become obvious. Research has not yet come into its own with respect to many of the smaller units of industry. The larger units have been able, because of their position, to pioneer the general movements. This pioneer work was possibly too hazardous for the small units to undertake; but now that the exploratory stage is pretty well over and trained personnel is available for executive positions there is no longer any reason why the smaller units of industry should not make full use of industrial research for their own advancement and welfare. It may be argued that to be efficient a certain minimum-sized laboratory is needed and that small organizations can not afford even this minimum size. There is much in favor of such an argument;

but a cooperative, or municipal, organization can overcome this difficulty. Such laboratories are coming into existence already.

I am of the opinion that, as time goes on, more and more research of the fundamental type will be necessary. This raises a serious question. Should such research be done in the actual industrial laboratory or would it be better, in most instances, to delegate it to the educational institutions?

Admittedly, some special cases will occur wherein the fundamental knowledge will be needed so quickly that the higher tempo of the industrial laboratory, for obtaining results, will be indicated; and other cases will occur where the need for secrecy is so great that it can not be entrusted elsewhere. However, the majority of cases should be such that they may be safely entrusted to the research staffs of our universities and colleges for study. This attitude should be encouraged whenever possible, for three reasons. First, the university staffs are generally able to bring a much broader vision to bear on these fundamental problems; second, where fundamental problems are being prosecuted in industrial laboratories they have a habit of being set to one side and forgotten when more urgent work develops; and third, the work thus given to the educational staffs will be of considerable value in educating future scientists to do more such work.

On the other hand, applied research should not be given to university or college staffs when the industrial unit is capable of performing this service for itself. Universities do not maintain the industrial tempo. Their staffs are not in the habit of working in the confidential capacity required for successful patent control, nor should they be asked to do so. Recently, many of our more technical schools have been developing a business department (usually called a foundation) for the purpose of successfully overcoming the above difficulties. It is sincerely to be hoped that such facilities will offer the small units of industry a means of solving many of their problems, both fundamental and applied.

Probably no other field holds more, and more varied, promises for successful industrial research than chemistry: success for the investigator who may satisfy his curiosity about the unknown with a fair share of honor and wealth; success for industry which may increase its payroll, its output and its profits; and success for the public who will reap the benefits of better health, higher standards of living and a safer world in which to live and travel. There are two catches to this charming picture, of which I am aware. First is the recent apathy the public has shown toward raising its standard of living. It is discouraging to develop new things or to open the way to better comfort just to have the public yawn and say, "So what?" Unless the public cooperates and raises its living standards as rapidly as industrial research makes it possible, unemployment is the inevitable result. I am not suggesting that the public go on a wasteful spending spree, ending up with little to show for it; but what I do mean is for the public to supply itself with better houses, better lighting, better radios and refrigerators, air conditioning and sound proofing, better automobiles, tires and gasoline, and the thousand and one useful articles that industrial research will be improving again when the war is over. The second catch, or rather handicap, to immediate expansion of our industrial research is the lack of properly trained personnel in the chemical fields. The war has already eliminated three years of the normal supply of college graduates and if the upward surge of research takes place after the return of peace, which we all hope for, we will find ourselves very short of professional chemists and chemical engineers. There will almost certainly be a decided rise in salaries as competitive industry again gets under way. This will not be bad for the

Expansion of Knowledge

chemists and chemical engineers who are already in industrial work, but its repercussions on the educational situation may be quite disastrous. The universities are in no position to bid, financially, for the services of the younger men who are needed as instructors, later as assistant and associate professors and still later as full professors and heads of departments. Industry should take heed of this situation before it gets out of hand. By ample fellowships in both size and number it should encourage many young men to remain in educational work in order that its own full needs can be met in the near future.

A few years ago our fellow scientists in the field of astronomy presented our minds with the intriguing concept of an expanding universe. Although this concept explains the observed fact that lines of the spectrum shift toward the red in proportion to the distance from the earth of the spiral nebulae, it can scarcely be subjected to the rigid examination of the reproducible experiment and, hence, must be held as speculative until such an examination can be devised. However, in quite a different sense, our environmental universe is definitely expanding. Few discoveries of any importance are made that do not open up still greater fields for future investigation and, consequently, more knowledge to be used by industrial research.

This accelerating expansion of potential fundamental knowledge constitutes an ever-growing stockpile of raw material ready for fabrication by industrial research. Obviously, this indicates a continuation of the expansion that industrial research has experienced during the past twenty-five years, irrespective of whether the "catching up" process is complete or not. It is difficult to develop any argument to contradict the desirability of expanding our industrial research in view of these realities; but there are other realities which will have a more quantitative effect than mere desirability. During the past twenty-five years industrial research has expanded ten times. Seventy thousand scientists are now engaged in it. Seventy thousand scientists are a rather large percentage of the total number available. Another sizeable group *must* remain in educational work, or the whole system will collapse. There is another group that will return with the armed forces which will be available after hostilities cease. However, it is doubtful if their number is much more than will be needed for replacement. Consequently, it is difficult to visualize any sizeable expansion until our supply of scientifically trained personnel can be increased through the normal process of education. This will require at least a few years after the war ends, probably three or four.

Once expansion does set in, management will again be faced by the problems of organization, location and unit size of the new laboratories to be built.

The past twenty-five years have established certain concepts of research organization that we may expect to endure for some time to come. It is scarcely necessary to discuss these accepted principles at this time. The research "team" as a unit in this organization has gained popularity in the recent past. The individuals of any particular team are chosen for their qualifications in their field of specialization, as it is related to the problem to be studied. This is a different approach to organization from the conception of a departmental head, with a variety of assistants. Both unit types have their places. The "team" is better adapted to the solution of problems involving two or more fields of science, while the "head," with assistants, works best on problems substantially confined to a single field. It has been observed that the problems involving multiple fields are becoming more numerous and hence the team conception is gaining in practice.

I have already mentioned that a minimum size of laboratory

Point of Diminishing Returns

is indicated for retaining efficiency. It would be dogmatic to attempt to define such a minimum, since many variable factors are involved in making any particular determination. It is a statement of principle rather than a quantitative value that is implied. On the other hand it is fair to ask the question, "Is there a maximum size, above which efficiency declines?" I have an instinctive feeling that there is. To make my point clear, it is necessary to define a laboratory as a group of research workers under the guidance of a single directing head. Obviously, a large building housing several such laboratories, with such things as library facilities, can be given a name and called a laboratory; but the unit size as above defined seems to me to have rather definite limitations. Again, this is a principle rather than a fixed value. The obviously controlling factor is the capacity of the research director to maintain an efficient understanding of the various problems for which he is responsible. In a way, this capacity is similar to that of a chess master playing simultaneous chess. Up to a certain number of games he is able to maintain a high playing standard, but, with a few more games added, the result is little more than a semi-automatic moving of pieces.

Another problem that eternally plagues management is location. There is no ideal location. There are advantages in being near the production center, there are advantages in being away from it. There is no advantage, that I am aware of, in complete isolation. No laboratory can be made so self-sufficient that it does not need services or supplies from the community wherein it operates. A laboratory operation located in a neighborhood lacking any such essentials can only result in delay and inefficiency. With such isolation also comes an inadequacy of social contacts between the professional employees and others engaged in similar activities. The result is deadening to the whole organization.

Location of Laboratories

The problem of location with respect to the production center is familiar to most of you. There are undeniable advantages in having the laboratory personnel well informed with respect to production problems and economies. This can best be obtained by proximity. On the other hand, the proximity of the research laboratory to production is an ever-present temptation to the production management to draw the laboratory into undertaking or studying the daily bread-and-butter problems which the production unit should be capable of solving for itself.

I know of two extremes within the same industry, one going so far that it disperses its laboratories among its various production departments, while the other operates its research laboratories at an overnight trip from the plant. Seemingly, both operations are equally successful. Possibly the solution for maximum results can be obtained by having two laboratories, one at the plant and another a few hundred miles distant. Ultimately, the problems each is best adapted to solve will find their proper atmosphere.

Duplication of effort is another problem that faces most research executives. It is very noticeable following some striking new piece of fundamental knowledge. Witness the tremendous activity that followed the discovery of deuterium. Practically every department of chemistry was busily engaged in some form of deuterium research within a few weeks. Little more came out of this vast effort than would have resulted from a centralized research.

I believe it is the purpose of our patent system to stimulate competitive research on applied subjects. Yet there are countless minor researches under way all the time in various laboratories that have no direct commercial value, that might very well be centralized, with excellent results and considerable savings. Call it "cooperative" or by any name you please, it should be encouraged. Duplication of effort is not always the result of one competitive laboratory not knowing what the other is doing. Sometimes it occurs within the confines of a single laboratory and within the supervision of a single director. Sometimes it is accidental and sometimes the rapid solution of some critical problem is so necessary that management is justified in setting two or more groups to work on it at the same time. Usually it is well to have the different groups attack it from different viewpoints. It is a situation, however, that requires skillful management, or the result may be disastrous. As long as esprit de corps can be maintained, perhaps with the stimulation of friendly competition, all is well; but once personal jealousies have developed, stagnation rather than progress is likely to result. It is essentially a problem of personnel management.

I should like to close with the suggestion that better public relations be developed by industrial research in general. Many of the difficulties that have been placed in the way of industrial research resulted from an ignorance on the part of the public and even of men in high places as to what it was all about. Ignorance breeds fear and fear motivates destruction. I am advocating that industrial research itself improve its public acceptance—not that industrial units merely advertise their own research departments. In fact this latter activity may be deleterious to the desired effect. Advertising copy has a way of romanticizing research, putting an air of mystery around the laboratory, calling it a "Home of Magic" or some other equally intriguing name. By these means the public is led to believe that industrial research is beyond their understanding and what the public does not understand it fears.

The public should be told just what research is when used by industry and how it benefits mankind. Then, too, as little secrecy as possible should be placed around new fundamental knowledge. It must be recognized that lacking any legal means of protecting its use, except secrecy, some secrecy is quite proper, but let it be as little as possible. Publish as soon as is compatible with safety and notify the public of this through the daily press and keep in mind what Dr. Kettering once said: "When you lock the laboratory door, you lock out more than you lock in."

Discussion: C. E. K. MEES

I have found it convenient in a discussion of this kind occasionally to remind ourselves of what we are talking about. I think it might be worth while to re-read the text of this discussion: "What should be the guiding principles and objectives for the commercial programs of industrial research and development organizations?" Now that is the fundamental question which we all have to deal with; it is the problem of research direction in industry.

What are the principles and objectives for the research program? I was asked that question a little while ago by a friend from England who wanted to know what I thought should be the objective of commercial programs for industrial research in that country, and I said, "You can't generalize completely, but I will take any industry you like and tell you what its objectives should be. Will you take an industry?" He suggested, "Well, let's take the boot and shoe trade." I replied, "Its objective should be better boots and shoes." He said, "That is a most astonishing statement," and continued, "I have discussed that with our people, and they said that our objective should be new and better ways of tanning leather." I stated, "Of course, that may enter into the making of better boots and shoes, but the objective of industrial research in the boot and shoe trade is better boots and shoes, and unless you keep your eye firmly fixed on that, you won't get what you are after." He declared, "I think that you should come over to England, not to preach science to the industrialists but to preach business to the scientists."

How are you going to organize industrial research to get better boots and shoes or better films and cameras, or whatever your job is? Well, at that point there enter systems of planning, and on this I am a complete heretic. The view that I take of planning is the same as the advice that Mr. Punch gave to those about to be married—"Don't." When I am asked how to plan, my answer is, "Don't." "But," my friends say, "you obviously plan."

One of my friends this morning said that he had discussed this heretical theory of mine with his practical research director, who said, "But that is ridiculous; I have looked through the Abridged Scientific Publications from the Kodak Research Laboratories. They have been publishing them for over thirty years, and there is great continuity in them. It is obvious that they are planned." As a matter of fact, our scientific work *is* continuous, not because it is planned but because our scientific men continue to work along the same lines.

As soon as you get a group of men together to do research, you find that you have to have an organization. You don't have to plan or organize the research itself, but you must have an organization among the men. This is usually expressed in a chart and, frankly, I don't think that those charts mean anything, though recently I have found them very valuable to meet the requirements of the War Labor Board and the Treasury Department.

Research is done by scientists. A scientist has attached to him some other people to help him. He has some unskilled helpers to do routine jobs which he tells them to do, and usually he has some skilled and trained helpers, whom he can direct for some time; and I say for some time, because if they are good they are presently split off into their own problems by mitosis and employ their own helpers. That is to say, research is done by unit groups; a research laboratory of any kind is made up of little cells, consisting of a scientist and a group of helpers, and as soon as the helpers get to be more than that particular man can direct—quite a small number—then a scientist from that group heads another group and forms another cell.

If you want to catalyze the research of the groups, all you have to do is to get them together and talk about what you want. For instance, if you want better boots and shoes, you just tell them so. Then they go away and presently they come back, after they have thought about boots and shoes, and they tell you what they have been thinking. They certainly haven't all been thinking the same thing. One man will come back and say, "What I think we chiefly need in the world is a better waterproof golf shoe." I think those of us who play golf will sympathize with that idea. All right; then you say, "Suppose you try and make one. Suppose you think about it." It won't be long before your research laboratory has organized itself, and then your job consists of keeping the men talking to each other, of going around and saying to a man, "I have just seen a report from Smith, and I notice that he is working on something that will be interesting to you. Have you talked to Smith?"

That is what the director mostly does. No director who is any good ever really directs any research. What he does is to protect the research men from the people who want to direct them and who don't know anything about it. As he protects and coordinates the work and watches what the men do, the director tells members of the staff things that have occurred among them and gets them working together. He has occasional meetings with them, and it may be that he says, "We are getting a little off the track here. We are a photographic laboratory and what we are doing is building high vacuum stills, and they haven't anything to do with photography." What he has to do then is to say, "Building high vacuum stills is a splendid thing to do but let's do it in another laboratory." So he builds another laboratory and starts making high vacuum stills.

(When I got one of my men to read the above, he said that it would give the impression that in our laboratory we work without any organization. I don't mean that, of course. We have the necessary organization for operating the laboratory. What I have been talking about are the guiding principles and objectives for the direction of the research itself.)

Discussion: ROGER ADAMS

Dr. Midgley has touched upon several points in his paper that relate to the universities and that pertain directly to the subject under discussion. As a representative of an educational institution, I believe a few additional comments on university chemistry departments, the training of young scientists, and fundamental chemistry in universities and industry are in order. Although what I shall say applies in general to chemists, physicists and engineers, my remarks will be primarily about chemists and chemistry.

The future of industrial research is dependent in no small way on the quality and training of the technical personnel which will be added to the research staff of industry. During the past ten years the supply of trained chemists has just about balanced the demand. The number available in the next five to seven years will be much smaller and not sufficient for the normal replacements of the present research laboratories without consideration of increase in size. In view of the avowed intention, or rather hope, of both large and small chemical companies to expand their research organizations immediately after the war, it is decidedly relevant to consider carefully the sole source of supply of new scientists—the universities.

The universities at the present time are in a tragic state. The policy of the U. S. Government and War Department is to eliminate completely during the war period the normal training of men qualified to specialize in science who are physically able to become soldiers. As a consequence, the students, both undergraduate and graduate, who are studying chemistry today are pitifully small in number, limited to those classified as 4F and a few women. There are, to be sure, many thousands of chemists in the armed services and in temporary civilian defense organizations who will be released when the war ends. A relatively small percentage of the total, however, will be as well qualified for chemical positions as before they entered the government service and a good proportion had not completed their academic studies. Many will require refresher courses in the universities or months of apprenticeship in industrial laboratories before they will be able to perform their assignments in a manner to be expected from their previous academic training. It is difficult to visualize how the universities can again reach their prewar status with respect to the number and quality of trained chemists graduated for at least another five years, and a longer period will be necessary if the war does not close reasonably soon. The U. S. government's attitude with respect to the training of chemists is in pointed contrast to that in England, Russia, France and, it is reported, even in Germany; for in these other countries during the war period highly qualified youths have been selected to receive regular training in science. The Imperial Chemical Industries has already taken steps to aid materially several of the larger educational institutions in England. They are offering several dozen very substantial fellowships, the recipients of which will serve as part-time teachers and part-time investigators in pure chemistry.

In the face of this dearth of trained chemists during the period of contemplated research expansion, the inclination of industry will be to search for the more capable university instructors and professors to add to their organizations. In fact, within the last few months, this tendency has already appeared. Four instances have come to my attention in which men in university chemistry departments between thirty and forty years of age, with most promising futures in pure science, have been offered industrial positions at three to five times their university salaries. In the next years when recovery in personnel in the universities is impossible, there is no better way of crippling the chemistry departments, of reducing them to mediocrity, and of thus lowering the standard of training of the young technical men of the future, than by adopting this policy. The universities have not had and will not have budgets adequate to compete with industry. Those of us interested in pure science and its future in this country can only attempt to persuade these men not to leave university work and hope they may obtain consulting positions to enhance their salaries sufficiently to fulfill their modest desires.

After the war, the university chemistry departments will also be confronted with the problem of obtaining additional staff members, in particular outstanding younger chemists, to help train the large flow of students who will inevitably enter the universities with contemplation of scientific careers. The usual salaries in the larger institutions in the United States for instructors in chemistry holding the Ph.D. degree have been and are from $2,000 to $2,500. This was an amount which formerly provided a living during that period when the man was acquiring experience in teaching and independent research. Since the war, however, with federal taxes, social security withholding, and generally increased costs, the net amount remaining for living expenses is now inadequate. To compete with industry for the few well-qualified men who will be available, the universities, with much lower salaries to offer, are facing a perplexing problem and one for which it is difficult to find a solution.

The present governmental policy, which practically eliminates the graduate students in chemistry, simultaneously and to the same degree eliminates research in pure science. Most of the fundamental scientific work in chemistry in the universities is accomplished with the aid of the graduate students during their period of training. Indeed, some of the more difficult work is done with the aid of post Ph.D. assistants, of whom there have been far too few in the past and now practically none. With the restricted remuneration that can be offered it will be even more difficult in the future to attract such assistants. The continuity of effort in pure or applied research is important in order to obtain significant results in a minimum of time. This continuity in pure science research has been disrupted to such an extent that years will be required to restore the volume and quality of results to the prewar level.

Pure science is the basis of all applied science. The great bulk of fundamental discoveries has come from the university laboratories of the world. Can industry therefore ignore the universities' situation? The sources for new material will be nearly dried up for a long period. The universities should receive help and complete cooperation of industry for selfish if for not more broadminded reasons.

Retention of Information

With the tremendous expansion of industrial chemical research laboratories in the last two decades, more and more long-range problems have been undertaken and more and more chemistry closer to the fundamentals is being studied. Basic discoveries of importance to pure science have evolved and many more will be forthcoming in the future. The concerns naturally keep such discoveries secret until they can be exploited from the applied standpoint and then protected. There is, however, very little inclination and certainly no feeling of obligation to reveal these basic discoveries to the pure scientists for further exploration from the academic angle. Indeed, it is seldom that such basic chemistry is disclosed until the issuance of patents requires it. The lapse in time after the discovery has first been made may be several years. University professors have in the past relied upon the scientific journals for information about fundamental discoveries. They have not been equipped as perhaps they should be to search for basic chemistry in the patent literature. Moreover, it is often not easy to distinguish the important from the unimportant in patents, even if a faithful review of them is made. The retention by industry of such information over a long period and the eventual disclosure merely in patents is not only a handicap to those engaged in pure research, but it affects industry directly in that the new scientists who are being trained for industry will be less adequately prepared than they otherwise would be.

Even though the training of scientists in universities has been open to criticism, and quite rightfully so, the fact remains that industry has been and will be in the future dependent on the universities for the embryo technical leaders. German chemical industry from its very inception has had the closest relationships with the universities and has always had their welfare at heart. I can only plead with the chemical companies in this country to take cognizance of the fact that healthy and progressive chemistry departments in the universities are all-important to them and cannot be regarded as something apart from the sphere of concern to industry.

Harry L. Derby

THE FUTURE OF

INDUSTRIAL RESEARCH

THE VIEW OF INDUSTRIAL MANAGEMENT

FOR WHATEVER VALUE some years of experience may have, I present a few impressions of the stern realities with which businessmen today find themselves confronted in carrying out the ideas which have their inception in research.

We are told by those who have studied the subject that the world is between three and four billion years old. Accepting this as beyond disproof, we learn that during this period there occurred violent chemical reactions brought about by the cooling of gases and vapors, and the formation of primary rocks and minerals. Life itself, whether or not originating from chemical processes, certainly came under their control. As soon as man was able to reason for himself he began chemical research. At an early stage he discovered how to make glass, how to dye his crude textiles, how to obtain the products of fermentation of sugar. Knowledge being cumulative, he expanded his area of investigation from a few basic chemicals to some hundreds of thousands presently known and successfully compounded. Coming generations will look back to our day and marvel at the crudeness we displayed in attacking the problems confronting us. Our successors, dealing not with hundreds of thousands but with millions of different compounds, will carry on this ever-expanding program of research in which you are so directly a part. Increased human desires, new and previously unthought-of horizons of opportunity—

all will spur on the efforts of the research chemist.

The tremendous advancement in technological development has made the present war the most terrible in the history of man, and at the same time has created opportunities such as this nation and the world have never before experienced. The present war has to a large extent resolved itself into a battle of science. New developments one after another in the form of new or improved weapons thrown into the battle frequently have meant at least temporary victory for the side originating the invention. The future security of our country, as Dr. Jewett has indicated, rests very largely on the future research of you men of science. At the same time, these developments have created opportunities such as this nation and the world have never before experienced.

As a nation we are indeed blessed in having natural resources filling the great majority of the present needs of our people. When we were denied access to such natural products as are found only in foreign lands, our scientists have been able to create a synthetic duplicate which in many instances produces superior results when used.

I have the greatest admiration and respect for the scientists. The man is indeed greatly blessed who has the ability to make successful application of scientific theories and secure the desired results. Businessmen, unlike the scientists, must deal with flexible and changing regulatory controls, some arising from economic conditions and some being imposed by government.

I am asked to discuss *the views of industrial management guiding the principles and objectives for the commercial programs of research and development.* My view of that question, if it had to be condensed into a sentence, would be that these programs will have served their purposes if as a result the life of man is prolonged, if his health and comfort are improved, if his happiness is enhanced, and if his productive ability and usefulness are enlarged. It seems to me that most of the new inventions, and particularly those with which this group is primarily concerned, contribute to that program. Your inventions and developments have enabled man to attain a speed on land and sea heretofore unknown. They have made flight through the air at maximum velocity possible. They have in many ways increased man's usefulness and increased his ability to produce more goods and services. The Roman emperors, with all their gold-trimmed chariots, never even visioned the luxury of riding over a modern concrete highway in a present-day automobile. The peoples of the nations have been brought closer together and become neighbors through your inventions. This may be for good, or for evil if wars are to continue, but the inventions and developments which you have created offer business opportunities of unprecedented scope.

Industrial research on a carefully organized and large-scale basis is a fairly recent development.

The sponsor of this Forum, Standard Oil Development Company, is marking the twenty-fifth anniversary of its establishment. Twenty-five years ago when its parent company—Standard Oil Co. (New Jersey)—set up this organization to bring various research activities together in a consolidated plan, the move was rather a novel one.

It is true that in the early years of this century a few companies organized research departments. But it is only since the first World War, which drew attention to the developments that had given Germany such industrial strength, that industrial research has become a major feature of our economic life. Before that time, there was mutual misunderstanding and lack of appreciation between men of science and men of business. Many managements strongly doubted that it was a proper function of industrial organizations to create research divisions and to support continuing broad research programs.

Certainly that situation is changed today. Research is now not only recognized as an integral part of business, but the United States has become the acknowledged world leader in this field. And although not all American industrial firms themselves operate research departments, none of them can successfully ignore the tremendous influence of research on the conduct of their business.

We who are management employees of businesses realize that research today involves much broader considerations than, let us say, simply the physical improvement of an existing product. It provides a guide for us in decisions bearing on the health and very life of our companies.

By way of illustration, twenty-five years ago the interurban electric trolley line was a familiar feature of American life. The companies operating those lines constituted an important service industry. Today the interurban trolley has disappeared almost completely, supplanted by autos, buses and trucks operating on highways. There has been a fundamental change in modes of transportation, and industrial research has had a large part in that change.

Similar changes or potential changes abound now. The management of a company in the light metals industry, for example, must be aware of research not only in light metals but also in plastics. And the reverse holds good for management in plastics.

Competition operates not only on its previous level but on new ones. It is no longer only rivalry among similar products in the same field. Today one kind of material competes with one or more totally different kinds which can be applied to the same use. There is competition between processes, and between raw materials as sources for the same product—for example, toluene comes from both coal tar and petroleum.

Personnel of 70 Thousand

I am confident that research in industry has not reached the ultimate in its scope and importance. According to figures compiled by the National Research Council, in 1920 about 300 industrial companies in this country employed 9,300 persons in research. By 1930 these numbers had grown to 1,625 establishments with personnel of 34,200. By 1940 the figures were 2,350 establishments and personnel of over 70,000. In other words, in twenty years there was more than a sevenfold growth in the number of people employed by American industry in research. Expenditures by industrial firms for this purpose have been estimated to be about $300,000,000 a year. The future outlook, I believe, is for this trend to continue and for research to occupy a still larger place in the plans of industrial management and to exert still greater influence on our economic life.

It becomes the businessman's function and responsibility to carry the inventions resulting from these great programs to their ultimate use. Through these new discoveries the workman finds employment in producing the goods and the owners of the business are rewarded for the risk of investing the needed capital.

Now, this all seems very simple and reasonable but unfortunately there are many difficulties in the present uncertain times which lie in the way of a successful fruition of any program. While not desiring to be overly pessimistic, nor in any sense to depreciate the value of your achievements, I would pose a few questions, the answers to which may to some extent influence the scope of future programs of research and development.

Abraham Lincoln said, "The patent system added the fuel of interest to the fire of genius."

Patents are important to you men and to organizations engaging in programs of research and development. A patent is a legalized monopoly for a limited period of time, and this monopoly is granted by the government for the purpose of encouraging men to spend effort and money to develop a new idea. It is also an assurance that if the new idea is commercially practical, the reward in the form of profits may be safeguarded. More than two million patents have been issued, many of which have no commercial possibilities. Those articles which are useful and unique usually find a ready market. Now, if the theory and basis of our patent system is to be radically changed, as some in government seem to wish; if large corporations or small corporations may no longer safely risk their stockholders' funds in research; if no longer the individual may be sure his idea will be protected; if these discoveries are to be free to all—then the incentive for burning the midnight oil disappears, and incentive has always been the motivating factor in industrial development in America.

In the early history of our country, had our patent program and financial system been patterned to suit the present ideas of these few, could Edison have been compelled by governmental edict to invent the electric light; could Marconi have been required to discover the marvels of wireless communication; would Kettering have found inspiration in bureaucratic compulsion?

When government no longer views with favor the operation of a business for profit and places in the way of success such a multiplicity of rules and regulations as to make it impossible to realize a profit; or when, through such rules and regulations and the resulting hindrances, goods cannot be produced economically—then private enterprise can no longer function successfully.

It is of more than passing importance that nearly one million small businesses ceased to exist during the year 1943. What percentage of these closed as a direct result of the war I do not know, but I am certain a large number of these businesses ceased to exist by reason of government regulations and interference beyond the direct and immediate necessity of war production.

Government cannot indiscriminately attack large corporations and at the same time be helpful to small business. What is large, and what is small? Your great successful enterprise was started as a small business by one man, and it grew to its present size through the combined efforts of all those engaged in its progress and enlargement over the years of its history. There are few corporations in America that did not have small beginnings. These businesses have grown through encouragement, not discouragement, by government.

At least until a business has grown to a point where it has reached a peak of economic production, with resulting lower cost of finished goods, is it not in the public interest that its progress be encouraged? Many of the great developments of recent years have originated in the laboratories of large corporations whose volume of business has made possible a liberal research budget.

We are hopeful that in a short time the millions of young men and women who have gone into the armed forces will be coming home. We are all concerned to see that they are given an opportunity to make their way, raise families and enjoy life in a free country. What are our responsibilities incident to their return? Surely the manufacturing corporations of America cannot absorb all these returning warriors. Never did manufacturing enterprises employ more than 25 per cent of available labor. The future of millions of these young people must be worked out through their engagement in small businesses, as individuals, on the farms, and in private enterprise of their own initiation. Their individual research and development for their own purposes must be encouraged and helped. They will find employment in industry to the extent that industry is able to develop and sell its products, including the new scientific developments and products of research. There will be expanding employment if the conditions are such that employers may gainfully increase their businesses.

America is the greatest market in the world, having the highest standards of living, and the daily individual necessities of our people are unobtainable luxuries to residents of many other countries. This is a great market for the products of research and development. If this were a discussion of the subject of commerce, I would add that the greatest obligation the nation has to its citizens is to protect their standards of living against the destructive competition of low-living-standard countries.

Not only is manufacturing industry a field for the development of new ideas but the farmer of today finds himself possessing the source of raw materials for new manufactured products resulting from the creative research of the laboratory.

I would pose another question for the consideration of this group. What is to be the status of the laboring man, including the returned soldier and sailor, in the postwar period? Will he be free to seek and hold employment when and where he chooses, at wages satisfactory both to himself and his employer, without undue interference on the part of government or labor organizations?

When management plans its research program these hindrances to which I have referred may not be safely ignored.

The horizons of research are limitless. As applied to a manufacturing business, research programs are economically sound if they have as an objective the production of better goods at lower cost. Industry's aim is to expand production. Men of research not only must tell us how to produce better goods at lower cost, but must discover new ways and materials to satisfy human needs.

Certainly everyone in this Forum has complete faith in the

future of America. I am sure we all believe that no faction or group can delay for long the progress of America. In the history of our nation there have been times when political and economic disturbances have retarded the acceleration of progress, but I believe that these present difficulties and interferences will be resolved, and that new and enlarged opportunities, many of them created by research, will enable this nation to continue the phenomenal advancement which is its birthright.

Discussion: R. K. BRODIE

In thinking about the subject of the guiding principles and objectives for the commercial program of industrial research from a management standpoint, since I have left manufacturing and think more in terms of the treasurer's reports and the like, my first thought is that, after all, anything we do is utilizing the shareholders' money, and our first obligation is properly to safeguard the investment of these people.

Along with that, of course, all progressive companies regard themselves as having an approximately equal obligation to their employees and to their consumers: the public.

Finding the balance in there is something that, so far as I know, no one has ever yet determined. But at least every move that is made within the organization should be directed toward the objective of properly serving the three groups.

This happens to be my silver anniversary year, too, in our industry; an industry that grew up in a veil of secrecy. During the first ten to fifteen years of my association with the business we were busy trying to straighten out the existing procedures and practices—trying to find out the fundamentals that underlie our operations—and so we have had a comparatively few years with what we would really call basic research.

Separating Trouble-Shooting

We did a lot of trouble-shooting, and as you all know, it is sometimes difficult to keep the research men out of trouble-shooting. The only solution to that problem is to set up a group of trouble-shooters and a group of researchers. If you have done that you know that whether you are next door or an overnight ride away, you can pretty well keep them apart.

In this picture we must consider, along with our desire to produce the best boots and shoes, or the best soap or the best cameras or whatever it may be, thus serving the consumer, that all of us in industrial organizations have an obligation to do fundamental research.

Our company hasn't done a great deal of it. We keep a group that we designate the basic research group, and it is our intention—and it has been our practice—as we develop some material that we think broad enough, and important enough, to publish it for the use of the scientific men of the country.

I think that is one of the fundamentals that should be included and one of the principles certainly of any industrial organization, to do basic research in so far as possible and yet protect the shareholders' money.

I was much interested in Mr. Derby's remarks about the tremendous effect of government regulations. All of us have had more than enough interference, and we realize how much it complicates the problem. We have been working with the Committee for Economic Development and are familiar with some of the problems that organization has run up against in trying to get others to plan for the future.

It is a very, very difficult thing for us to set up a research program, let's say, leading to a new product, and be certain of what we are going to come out with, and we can appreciate the great difficulty that smaller companies have in planning their future, and thus helping in this economic situation and the maintenance of high levels of employment.

As Mr. Derby has pointed out, the ability of small business to employ people is going to be a tremendous factor in the future of the employment situation in this country, and it is a problem to which we must give our full thought. We must encourage the small business as far as possible. It is our experience that merchandising is so much more important than patents or knowledge of processes—provided, of course, you aren't stopped because of a patent situation—that a merchandising program can easily offset any slight disadvantage resulting from doing something along technical lines to assist the smaller manufacturers in their preparation for this postwar situation.

Discussion: LAMMOT DU PONT

One of the things that impressed me most when I became engaged in the chemical industry was this matter of fundamental research. It seemed to me that fundamental research was the ideal type of research, but in later years I was faced with the problem of what fundamental research is and, in my crude way, not being a scientist at all, I came to the conclusion that fundamental research is the examination into some question, the prospective results of which seemed to be entirely useless. Why should that be a desirable field for work? Why, I think the explanation is that the thing that appears to be useless very frequently turns out to be of great use, and in a way which is entirely unexpected.

What is fundamental research today is applied research tomorrow. I believe in the end it will always turn out that way.

I can think of no science, no line of research, that looks more "fundamental" today than astronomy. How can the investigation of the stars and other heavenly bodies have any application to what we are doing on earth? But the reason that astronomy seems to be so inapplicable is that we don't know all about astronomy. When we do we will find the application.

One of the previous speakers has said that the best *direction* of research is not to direct it. I don't think that is correct in the sense in which I am speaking. The division between fundamental research in industry and applied research is a subject for direction, and the man who directs fundamental research in industry, and directs it properly, is the one who makes the success in that industry.

Discussion: FRANK A. HOWARD

For about twenty-five years we have been trying to make a better application of physical research in industries that are thought of as chemical.

Dr. Millikan started to help us on that when in 1919 we attacked Mr. Kettering's favorite problem, "What makes the engine knock?"

But for some reason we have never been able to find how to use physical science properly in our own industry. And our situation is quite similar to that of the petroleum industry in general and, I think, to that of the chemical industries. I don't know what the difficulty is, but I know it is there.

In the petroleum industry, outside the field of geophysics, we have done effective laboratory work with physics only during the last five years. The physical inspection methods of ultra-violet refraction and absorption and infrared spectroscopy now enable us to do literally in minutes what used to take us hours and days to do. But that is about the only use we are making of the modern science of applied physics, as distinguished from the straight engineering sciences.

I merely lay this before you as one of our fundamental difficulties in facing the future of research. We must bring about a better wedding between physical research and the so-called chemical sciences and chemical engineering, which underlie the process industries of today.

The university men with whom I have discussed this problem during the last few years have all acknowledged the problem, but none of them has suggested any solution.

Discussion: CHAIRMAN C. F. KETTERING

The problem that Frank Howard has discussed is one in which we also are interested, because we have very high-grade physicists come to us and say, "Why is it in the motor car industry you don't use any physicists, when the electrical business has a lot of them and the chemical business has a lot of them? Why is it you don't use them in your industry?"

The only answer we had is that we *did* have some thirty million automobiles running around on the streets. Nevertheless, here is what we have tried to do in setting up the problem.

I think that the nomenclatures, the methods of teaching, and so forth, have produced useless divisions of the same subject.

To me an engineer is a fellow who works with something tangible (indicating gavel). He works in grams, and we call his work physics, and applied physics is engineering.

The engineer works and the carrier of his energy is a tangible thing. It is the railroad train, it is the airplane, it is the motor car, and so forth.

The chemist is an engineer who works with a unit called a molecule, and the laws of physics hold in that molecule just as positively as they do in this gavel. So the size of the carrier of his energy relationships is different.

Failure Also Teaches

The electrical worker deals with atoms and electrons, and his carrier is still smaller.

So we think that if we understand the relationship of the energy carrier to the energy itself, that helps to clarify the situation.

When I was in school one of the great pet controversies was whether the student in the physics department knew how to weigh anything on a chemical balance, and vice versa. In other words, we can never see any difference between chemistry and physics or between biology and physics. They are all material and energy relationships in which molecules, atoms and so forth are involved, and calling them different sciences and adding a lot of Latin and Greek doesn't help the situation.

We are getting into the Tower of Babel as far as technological lingo is concerned, and we need to get down into common words. Some time ago an effort was made to prepare a dictionary of scientific terms. As I recall, we got as far as the word "atom." We didn't get any further because we couldn't reach any agreement. Then they finished it up by calling it "a glossary of the probable meanings of these words."

In industrial research we need not try to save face so much as to get facts. Whether you are a chemist or a physicist or an engineer, one of the things that you have to do when you come to work for us is to sign a pledge, without writing it down, that you don't have to defend what you don't know. Therefore, your willingness to admit what you don't know is not held against you.

We have always said we thought we could train men to become inventors by the simple process of saying, "It is not a disgrace to fail. You are out of school now, and you don't have to be examined any more." From the time a chap is six years old until he graduates from college he is examined three or four times every year, and if he flunks once he loses out. But we say, "Among inventors, if you succeed once, you are in. But we don't want you to fail miscellaneously; we want you to fail intelligently. Therefore, you set the thing up, and there isn't one chance in a thousand that the thing will *work* the way you expect it to, but it won't *fail* the way you expect it to, either." That is the way you learn.

The over-all relationship between education and research is extremely important. There is no difference between the test tube that we have in the university and the test tube we have in the industrial laboratory, and the man who was shaking one yesterday is shaking the other today, but for some reason many people think that there is a change of habit when a man goes from one to the other. We don't think so, at all, and never have. Therefore, we think that the cooperative exchange of industrial research people with the universities is an all-round gain. Maybe in this way we can analyze some of our rather complicated research problems to the point where they can be treated as isolated technological problems, with the economic considerations eliminated.

You can't expect to have an educational institution analyze your economic problems, your sales problems, and so forth, and pick out the right technological development.

As Mr. du Pont said, the training is all-important in research. But the question arises: How far ahead must you start on research before the salesman can carry the product on the road? In our particular line we say we work from ten to fifteen years ahead of the product. We call that research. We divide up our research program in this way: About twenty-five per cent of our total man hours goes into service to our divisions; another twenty-five or thirty per cent goes into sample making, that is, making working samples which are not products, but from which a product can be designed; and the other forty-five or fifty per cent is spent in long-range pure science, or physical and chemical research, in which we begin to orient *into useful information* the factors which are not yet quite in a tangible form.

As an example of this latter type of work, consider the research in combustion. Our first contact with Frank Howard, many, many years ago, occurred when we were working on the question of what caused the knock in an engine. We still don't know—but we do know a lot of things that don't cause knock. That work has been of a long range, and it really is concerned with fundamental thermodynamics.

It has been perfectly amazing how you can take some of the factors that you know, and by trying them over a large range of conditions, achieve your results. We have had that result in Diesel engine development. The engine was very old, long before we had anything to do with it. We have succeeded now in getting pretty high thermal efficiencies even in a 1,000-kilowatt Diesel. Such an engine, running at, say, 850 kilowatts, will now have a thermal efficiency as high as thirty-eight per cent. We didn't get that result by observing fundamental laws of thermodynamics alone, even though we did use them, any more than we have to be perfect in grammar before we can write a sentence. We "wrote the sentence" afterward that would fit the laws of thermodynamics, but we had to do an enormous amount of cut-and-try work which could not have been figured out in advance.

So, we have always to use all the factors—the best science, the best projects, the best mathematics, the best physics, the best chemistry—to get what we call our "first approximation." It gets into final form only after a lot of very tedious work.

Once I explained this process to an educator. He wanted to know how we did this particular job; I showed him, and he asked, "Isn't that very tedious?"

I replied, "It is *very* tedious."

He stated, "There ought to be a better way of doing that."

I said, "We admit that."

But there is one thing that the industrial researcher must not do—he must never be irked by tediousness. If he is going to achieve these advanced developments he has to take the best that all of the sciences afford, bring them together into these "first approximations" and then experiment and experiment, because so many things don't work in the new combinations just as the old theory would indicate.

Take this great subject of oil, petroleum, fuels, lubricants, and so forth. Since the Standard Oil Development work started in 1919 we have seen a revolution in all phases. For example, the fundamental laws of lubrication are no longer what they were then. Then there is the question of this thing we call "combustion." We get combustion with paraffins, and the word "paraffin" means "little affinity"; but detonation certainly isn't very little.

One of the fundamental courses that industrial researchers have to follow is to let the problem be the boss. We must not try to make it like something else. Petroleum is like petroleum, and it is going to stay that way, and the progress is made when we swing around and play on petroleum's home lot.

When poor Dr. Diesel made his engine forty or fifty years ago he had to put it in the place of a steam engine, so it had to be like a steam engine. Then when we came out with the automobile engine, the Diesel had to be like gasoline engines. All we did in our development work was to let them be like Diesel engines.

So let these things be what they want to be. If I had to set up a forward-looking program for industrial research, I would say: "Pick out the problem, pick out the best men you have, and let the job be the boss from then on."

Remedies for Deficiencies

Introductory Remarks: R. W. GALLAGHER

This war has produced amazing instances of American resourcefulness. When we recall the simple faith that accompanied us up to the very brink of threatened destruction, unprepared for our defense, perhaps the fact that we are still alive is itself a near miracle. What this nation has done since December 7, 1941, to remedy our deficiencies is almost unbelievable.

Not the least of our accomplishments is the recovery of our rubber supply. The Japanese had us in a tight hole when they took Singapore. From the Malay Peninsula and Dutch East Indies came practically all of our crude rubber, of which we were the world's largest consumers. Without rubber we could not have built planes, jeeps, trucks or tanks.

The Baruch Committee summarized this in its famous report put out early in 1942. There it said:

"Of all critical and strategic materials, rubber is the one which presents the greatest threat to the safety of our nation and the success of the Allied cause. Production of steel, copper, aluminum, alloys or aviation gasoline may be inadequate to prosecute the war as rapidly and effectively as we could wish, but at the worst we still are assured of sufficient supplies of these items to operate our armed forces on a very powerful scale. But if we fail to secure quickly a large new rubber supply, our war effort and our domestic economy both will collapse. Thus the rubber situation gives rise to our most critical problem."

That was two and one-half years ago. The crisis has been passed. Today there are synthetic rubber plants in the United States capable of producing 836,000 long tons of synthetic rubber per annum. The ultimate capacity looks to be an estimated annual production of more than a million tons.

The pressing need for a substitute rubber made questions of

type, cost, processes, etc., of little importance rated against the early production of some kind of a usable article. In the words of the Baruch Committee, the authorities were to "bull" the operation through. It was the government's privilege to proceed in this manner because it was supplying all but 5 per cent of the new money going into the synthetic rubber program. With the relatively comfortable situation which we have today, we should begin to make long-range plans for keeping and perfecting those operations which will put synthetic rubber into a close competitive position as regards natural rubber.

The author of the next paper retired as rubber director with the issuance of a valedictory report on August 31. He said that the major part of the problem had been so far completed that there was no longer any need for continuing the office of Rubber Director as a separate function. It is news of the first magnitude when an officeholder liquidates his job and retires himself to private life.

INDUSTRIAL RESEARCH

BY SMALL BUSINESS AND BIG BUSINESS

NATIONAL DEFENSE as a problem does not end when this war is over. Everyone knows that this war will be finished with a lot of potential weapons, perhaps forged by science, not having been used. There is no use in our saying that we won't use them. There is always the other fellow.

In the old days the new weapons came from the machine shop. They were mechanical. Today they are very likely to come out of the process industries. They are closely tied in with the economy of any nation. We have to recognize the fact that we are where we are today in this war very largely because of the contribution of research organizations working in the setting in which they were born, working with the engineering groups, the operating groups, the executives with whom they had worked for years, largely in big industry.

Today it is all too common for the politician who wishes to be elected to have for one of his planks the destruction of large industry or the whittling down of large industry. I am a small businessman. I am all for small business, but I don't think that there is any necessity of a small businessman taking the attitude that you have to destroy big business in order to have healthy small business. There is no reason the two shouldn't live together.

The last two decades have seen a big change in our business ethics, in our code of ethics. To me it is getting better all the time. It will undoubtedly get still better. We have a great many corporations today, big corporations, whose code of ethics is so good that I am willing to take my chances anywhere selling in competition with them.

And I think that big or small, we have to recognize the fact that for our national defense we have to keep alive the working teams of scientists, engineers (chemical, mechanical, electrical), the operating forces and the executives who understand each other and have worked together. If we don't, we will be easy picking for anyone who comes along.

With them we have to keep alive a healthy and rational patent policy and patent system. We have to protect private initiative. We have to encourage the small as well as the large business. We cannot afford to be destructive; we cannot afford to allow the doctrine of technological unemployment to stick up its ugly head at the expense of a maximum of research—healthy research.

If the big companies have committed sins—they probably have, along with all the rest of us—I think their greatest sin has been that of not being vocal enough. I wonder if their part in synthetic rubber, in high octane gasoline, in many other parts of this war, will be well enough remembered in the next decade? I think every one of us is determined today that we will be supporters of a large, healthy, strong navy when this war is over. It is just as important for us to see that we support the doctrine of a healthy research body, ready to go to work in another emergency if it comes along.

There are certain types of research which must be carried on during peacetime which don't show an immediate prospect of profit and will need government help. But this should stop with those things which are purely for war or national defense and let the private initiative and business competitive system carry as much of the load as possible.

The Job Done by Industry

There are great dangers ahead, there is a lot of fuzzy think-ing being done, and the initiative which has brought about the power that enabled us to do the job that has been done by in-dustry, not government, in this war, has to be kept alive.

It is all right to glorify the Rubber Director and all right to glorify the Petroleum Administration for War, and all right to glorify the achievements of the Army and the Navy and everyone else in the government field, but you and I all know that it was industry that did the job, and that industry and its research must be kept healthy.

Discussion: FRANK A. HOWARD

Implicit in these discussions is the assumption that we all have the same thing in our minds when we speak of industrial research. It may be worth while to examine this question briefly. When my company was planning its technical pro-gram in 1919, we tried to get a better understanding of the con-cept called industrial research by dividing it into its component parts. It seemed clear to us that new industries and the ad-vancement of old industries depend first of all on increasing the sum of human knowledge, and of course, that is the func-tion of scientific research. But they depend even more on the new application of existing knowledge, and that is develop-ment. The amount of scientific knowledge already available which ought to be applied to an industry and has not yet been applied is almost always far greater than the new contributions to human knowledge which any industrial research organiza-tion can hope to make. Quantitatively, therefore, industrial re-search is largely development, and the most accurate term for it is "research and development." In our case, the probable ratio of development effort to research effort was so large that we called our new organization a development company, and the use of the term "development department" or "development company" to designate the research and development organization of an industrial unit is now quite common.

The third component of industrial research is the unpredictable one, invention. By invention, new concepts seem to appear suddenly on the earth, or more commonly, new applications of existing knowledge seem to spring into existence. But while invention is unpredictable, the record shows that in an environment of organized research and development effort, the inventive mind reaches a level of productiveness beyond all past experience.

These three—scientific research, development, and invention —seem to be the main components of technical progress in industry. It is therefore the function of industrial research to harness these three components in a sustained common effort, and to keep the effort headed in the right direction.

PART TWO

THEME

*"How can small business
serve itself and be served by industrial
research and development?"*

RESEARCH BY THE

BUSINESS ITSELF

I BELIEVE QUITE SIMPLY that the small company of the future will be as much a research organization as it is a manufacturing company, and that this new kind of company is the frontier for the next generation.

The business of the future will be a scientific, social and economic unit. It will be vigorously creative in pure science, where its contributions will compare with those of the universities. Indeed, it will be expected that the career of the pure scientist will be as much in the corporation laboratory as in the university.

Internally this business will be a new type of social unit. There will be a different kind of boundary between management and labor. All will regard themselves as *labor* in the sense of having as their common purpose learning new things and applying that knowledge for public welfare. The machinist will be proud of and informed about the company's scientific advances; the scientist will enjoy the reduction to practice of his basic perceptions.

Economically such small scientific manufacturing companies can, I believe, carry us quickly into the next and best phase of the Industrial Revolution. A thousand small companies, each employing 2,000 people (including fifty scientists), grossing $20,000,000 each, spending $1,000,000 on research, would do this:

A New Type of Company

Employ 50,000 research men;
Spend $1,000,000,000 on research and engineering;
Employ 2,000,000 people directly;
Contribute $20,000,000,000 to the national income
  directly, and much more indirectly.

And year by year our national scene would change in the way, I think, all Americans dream of. Each individual will be a member of a group small enough so that he feels a full participant in the purpose and activity of the group. His voice will be heard and his individuality recognized. He will not feel the bitter need, now felt by countless thousands, for becoming a member of a great mystic mass movement that will protect him and give him a sense of importance. These small groups will be located in the periphery of large cities and distributed through the countryside. Thus, the worst phase of the Industrial Revolution—the slums of Charles Dickens which still disgrace nearly every one of our large cities—will be gone.

How, specifically, will the scientific manufacturing company of the future operate? How will it achieve the income indicated above? What articles will it make?

First of all, this new company will start by contemplating all of the recent advances in pure science and in engineering. Its staff will be alive to the significance of newly available polyamide molecules, the cyclotron, radar technics, the details of new processes for color photography, and recent advances in enzymology. A group of fifty good scientists contemplating one of these fields and inspired by curiosity about them and a determination to make something new and useful, can invent and develop an important new field in about two years. This new field will be a monopoly for the group—a monopoly in the best sense of the word—because it will derive from justifiable patents on important inventions, and from know-how deliberately acquired by the group.

Who can object to such monopolies? Who can object to a monopoly when there are several thousands of them? Who can object to a monopoly when every few years the company enjoying that monopoly revises, alters, perhaps even discards its product, in order to provide a superior one to the public? Who can object to a monopoly when any new company, if it is built around a scientific nucleus, can create a new monopoly of its own by creating a wholly new field?

The company that is spending as large a proportion of its total income as I have indicated on research and engineering will carry its process development much further than is customary in small business. Basic research will be so thorough that the equipment required for manufacturing will be light weight and automatic, requiring relatively small capital investment and relatively few operators. The essential technic for increasing the amount of work to be done during the next generation should be the multiplication of fields of activity rather than the multiplication of operators required in any particular activity.

A small company by spending much on research and development can afford to change its product every few years to meet the demands of its market. As a result of the lavish expenditures in research it can make for a few hundred thousand dollars enough machinery to produce many millions of dollars worth of its products. As its customers' requirements change from year to year it can afford to alter or discard this relatively inexpensive manufacturing equipment.

Furthermore, the small business of the future will be in a much better position to experiment with new markets. I believe it is pretty well established now that neither the intuition of the sales manager nor even the first reaction of the public is a reliable measure of the value of a product to the consumer. Very often the best way to find out whether something is worth making is to make it, distribute it, and then to see, after the product has been around for a few years, whether it was worth the trouble.

This kind of experimentation is not possible if the production equipment is as expensive as it has been in the past. An investigation of public taste by actual marketing is feasible only when the manufacturer has made his big investment in research rather than in equipment. A research program is never a failure. Every incident in its history will prove to be an educational factor in the next investigation undertaken. Almost inevitably the research program which appeared to have failed several years ago results in new knowledge that some clever individual finally adapts to his company's needs.

Thus, the longer a company has been carrying on an extensive research program the richer relatively that company is. This wealth does not appear on the balance sheet. It manifests itself each time a new demand is made on the company. It also appears as a social factor because all the members of the group feel that they share a common wealth of knowledge. No matter how thoroughly and promptly the results of the scientific work have been published there remains a somewhat intangible body of materials that cannot be published but which the group draws on constantly in its new production efforts. Incidentally, one of the great benefits that the university scientist derives from becoming a member of such an industrial group is the acquisition of this unpublished knowledge.

Before summarizing the benefits that the company can derive from doing its own research, I should like to comment on the relationship between the academic scientist and industry. President Conant of Harvard urged a few weeks ago, at the meeting of the American Chemical Society, that industry not destroy the sources from which they derive their good men.

President Conant fears that industry may offer such high salaries to competent scientists that they will leave the universities. It seems to me that the sensible response for industry to make is this: "We will not take the good men away from the universities, but we should like to share them. We feel that the industrial environment can be as stimulating to the development of pure science as the university has been. We should like to bring into industry the kind of professional ethics that characterize the relationship between pure scientists. We should like to have knowledge of the scientific method permeate our organizations. Let us share your scientists and we will teach them many new aptitudes."

Any honest scientist will recognize that there are fads and trends in the pursuit of pure science and that many competent young men waste many years in activities in which they learn little and contribute little. Industry can provide a much larger field of inquiry for pure science and much greater human stimulus to many of the young scientists than are now provided by the university. In short, a continuum between pure science in the university and pure science in industry should stimulate and enrich our social system.

Finally, the small business that incorporates its own research department is adaptable, mobile, socially integrated and profitable. It finds new markets for big business and molds the product of big business to the transient demands of an evolving technical society. The small scientific business is individualized yet organized, free from political domination but a successful contributor to the solution of our great social problems.

One of the great problems that confront the small company which makes large investments in research is that it is in imminent danger of becoming a large company. The problem cannot be solved by spending still larger sums on research because—almost by definition—that would make the company grow still faster.

The only solution that has occurred to me is this: Perhaps when the small business has grown to have several thousand employees, it should consider division by fission. Perhaps some of the younger—and the older—men should take one of the numerous products which the laboratories will have developed, and base a new and similar company on this product. Ideally the parent company should control the new company for only a few years, setting it free for a life of its own as soon as it has the necessary strength. While "normal" human acquisitiveness might make this seem a radical proposal at the moment, it may be possible to show that membership in a chain of small interests, without control, might be more profitable to any member than domination of a few related companies. I certainly hope it can be made to appear adequately profitable because it seems obvious that all other motivations for growth by fission are healthy ones: increase in good new products, increase in personal opportunity, increase in paternal gratification, increase in stimulus and freedom for formation of new scientific industries.

RESEARCH BY
TRADE ASSOCIATIONS
AND COOPERATIVE GROUPS

IT SEEMS TO ME that, before we can answer the question, "How Can Small Business Serve Itself and Be Served by Industrial Research and Development?" it is necessary to determine what is expected of industrial research and development. Do we expect it to answer some immediate crisis or are we seeking to assure the company's future? What is the real objective? With the objective fixed, a number of possible methods are available for its accomplishment. Some seem to answer the immediate objective but show obvious weaknesses in the long-range benefits which all business, large or small, must cultivate. Some seem to present the long-range answer, but miss important, current problems.

I think that much of the difficulty in defining the objective will arise from any attempt to segregate the problems of a large company from those of the small organization. Is it not true that, industry by industry, the problems of both large and small components are similar? Is it not true that they vary in importance, both immediate and long range, only in a matter of degree?

In my experience, one of the most serious universal problems existing in all phases of industry is the lack of understanding of research, what may be expected of it, and how its products may be effectively used. This is a condition which can be solved only through the experience and wisdom of the policy-making management. It must be realized that research cannot be purchased by the pound, yard, or gallon. It is not an article of commerce. Also, it is difficult for research, as represented by those who work in the field, to realize its responsibilities to society as a whole and particularly to that segment of society which they have been chosen to serve.

In discussing the question, I am assuming that we are attempting to determine by what methods industrial research and development may best be implemented to promote the interests, present and future, of a company or the industry of which it is a part.

Personally, I do not see that the problems of so-called large and small businesses in the same industry differ except in matter of degree. Some of the problems confronting the large enterprise may be more critical than a similar problem in a small enterprise because of the size of the organization, and vice versa. But the basic problems are fundamental problems which are germane to the raw materials, their processes, the products of the industry, or the use for which its products are intended. These are the more important problems for the industry and its components to attack. These promise the more fruitful long-range returns. These would seem to be the problems to which the industry's attention should be directed collectively.

Because it has become indelibly fixed in my mind that the problems of a small segment of an industry probably have as much effect on the overall condition of an industry as the problems inherent in a large unit of the same industry, I believe that greater progress for the industry as a whole, and therefore for its components, lies in a collective attack upon the problems of fundamental science which lie at the root of most production and development problems. Mind you, I do not think there is any panacea. I do not believe that research individually or collectively can be expected to be the answer to a crisis. But it can and will provide the foundation for sound progress.

Many of our thinking industrial leaders view the future and its problems as representing an era of industrial competition —not among segments of an industry but among the industries which the collective segments comprise. The horizons of the industries must be widened in order that suitable outlets for the tremendously increased production capacities may be found. Inevitably, the search of these widened horizons must be founded on knowledge of the use requirement of the end-product and the fundamental characteristics of the products which are necessary to fulfill those use requirements. Education of the consumer must be based upon proved facts rather than upon high pressure salesmanship and wishful thinking, for the outlets *must endure* because, if they are unstable, any planning which relies upon continuance of these outlets will be based upon a fallacy.

One of the leaders in the industry with which I am most closely associated, in describing the ideology of The Institute of Paper Chemistry, made the following statement which I quote: "What seems to me to be the outstanding feature of the Institute is a recognition that man is the common denominator of all problems. Politically and economically, we speak of 'systems'. Industrially, we refer to competition for markets. Actually, everything resolves itself into the character and education of men. In our businesses, we are inclined to think of the future in terms of materials and machinery. In the final analysis, however, an industry's success is dependent upon the wisdom and stature of the men who comprise it. While industries compete in services and products, their ultimate competition is for manpower. The paper industry must see that it gets at least its share of outstanding young men, wherever they may live or whatever their previous interests may have been. If we succeed in this, we shall succeed in all else."

The men to whom he refers must be scientifically trained. They must have contact with the problems of the industry, both scientific and economic. They must have acquaintance with and knowledge of the history and tradition of the processes and materials which comprise its business. They must have an appreciation of the tortuous paths which have been traveled by pioneers in the field to arrive at the existing empiricisms. They must understand the fields of fundamental science which are related to the raw material their industry uses, the processes through which it passes, the products which result, and their use. They must learn to harness scientific phenomena and develop their application for the benefit of the industry of which they are a part. Early, they appreciate their stake in the future of the industry with which they are connected and realize that they are part of a unit which collectively can profit only by the scientific progress of their industry. They must understand that their personal opportunity for reward and future is inseparably linked with this collective progress.

One of the many reasons I endorse an industry's collective research program is that I believe that it is imperative that research be accompanied by a training of men in order that the fruits of research may be translated into production. And I further believe that training of manpower for the industry without attendant research is like inbreeding—it sharpens the line of current practice, crystallizes prevailing empiricisms, and bars the door to industrial progress.

The cooperation of individual competing companies within an industry, the pooling of their research resources and of their production information during World War I, gave individual industries an unbelievable impetus; new markets, and new products, even new industries evolved. The example of research accomplishments attendant to the prosecution of World War I led to a condition that might well be classified as research worship rather than an understanding of research. The need for research within any one industry was not universally appreciated; the understanding within any industry of what could be accomplished by research was not sufficiently clear for a program to emerge.

We all know that during the Nineteen-Twenties individual companies figured that research was a good thing to buy—it was good advertising copy! We can all recall examples of the window-dressing type of research that characterized that era. We all know the story of the organization whose management avidly pursued the pot of gold that lies at the foot of the research rainbow on the theory that if one research man working three years could bring about a specific development, three research men could do it in one year, and three hundred could reach the goal in approximately thirty days! And we are all well acquainted with the result of the application of that theory. We all know instances of educational institutions' entry into the field of consultation both in advisory capacities and as functional units. We all have had contact with some of the early, sporadic attempts for the collective farming out of research.

For purposes of this discussion, I would like to present what I believe to be one of the first constructive, collective programs on the part of an industry to provide for itself what its leadership believed would best protect the future of that industry. The program was set up in 1929 after "Black Friday." Nineteen paper mills, located in one state, comprising 90 per cent of the total tonnage of paper produced in that state, joined together in the organization of an educational and research institution for their industry. The institution was designed to train men at the graduate level, particularly for one industry, the paper industry. Its plan was to use the facilities of the institution for the industry, first, as a training medium and, secondly, as a research center for the benefit of the industry—not as a substitute for but as an adjunct to the individual companies' research activities. The faculty of the institution was to be used for the benefit of the industry both as teachers who would multiply the benefits of their training through the student body and as prosecutors of research serving as a unit.

It was intended to develop at the institution a comprehensive scientific library and to gather in that library all the available scientific literature pertaining to the industry, its chemistry, and its processes. The institution was to be provided with the best available equipment and scientific instruments, these to be used not solely as demonstration media but also as experimental tools.

Five types of research were to be carried on at the institution, all intended to be of service to the industry:

1. Fundamental research, to include the specific staff research projects initiated to provide a background for broader investigation.

2. Scientific research carried on by the students for their masters' theses or doctors' dissertations, as a part of the requirements for an academic degree.

3. Research on general problems which should be of interest and ultimate benefit to the industry as a whole.

Findings from these three classes of research were to be available to all the mills supporting the program. After a period of two years had elapsed, it was expected that the results of these three types of research would be published for the benefit of the industry as a whole.

4. Researches of a fundamental nature on specific problems presented to the staff by an individual mill or a group of such mills supporting the program or accepted from the trade association which represented the whole industry. Results from

this type of research, whether patentable or not, would belong solely to the mill or mills or, in the case of the trade association, to the association initiating and financing the research project.

5. Research of a confidential nature on specific problems presented by allied industry. By allied industry was meant one which supplied materials or equipment to the paper industry. Any problems which showed promise of ultimate benefit to the paper industry would be accepted from its allies. These might include the development and application or the adaptation of a product or a process. Findings which would result from this type of research, whether patentable or not, would belong solely to the company initiating and financing the research project.

All students, faculty, and staff were to be under patent waivers to the institution. All patents or patentable ideas originating within the institution were to belong to the institution and through it to its supporters or, as has just been explained, to the company or group who initiated and financed any specific project. All scientific members of the staff were to be fully employed by the institution. They were not to be permitted as individuals to do any consultation. All consultation was to be undertaken by the institution as a unit. All department heads and staff members were to participate. Thus, those seeking assistance from the institution would benefit by the combined training of the staff and by the approaches indicated by their special scientific training in varied fields rather than the restricted approach of one individual with research training in one narrow field of science.

The faculty was to be composed of men whose prior activities had demonstrated their ability to survive in competition, practicing their specialties. It was felt that through such an organization it would be possible for segments, large and small, of the industry to avail themselves of facilities both of personnel and equipment which could not be economically provided by an individual company no matter how large. The researches of this institution were not intended to substitute for the individual company's research activities but to supplement them through facilities not otherwise available.

That was the purpose of the founding of The Institute of Paper Chemistry at Appleton, Wisconsin, in 1929. That is the plan upon which the institute was based. Those were its objectives. It started as a provincial organization with a national ambition. Its support has grown. Beginning with nineteen individual companies, its support now flows from one hundred. At its beginning, 90 per cent of the production of one state was represented in its support. Now, 70 per cent of the total production of pulp, paper, and board of the entire nation is represented in the support of its program.

During its life, it has handled over 1,100 projects. It has produced four texts, three definitive books, thirteen chapters in books or definitive compilations in related fields, over three hundred scientific publications with an additional hundred-odd temporarily impounded. Its *Library Notes*, containing current abstracts from 179 publications, foreign and domestic, are circulated monthly, to its supporters and scientific libraries. Its *Quarterly Research Bulletin*, which covers the general and academic research program, goes only to its supporters. Some two hundred patents are based upon its researches. One hundred sixty-three bibliographies have been completed by its editorial staff, one of the most comprehensive of which contained 2,963 annotated abstracts with a total of 694 pages.

Its staff, originally three in number, has grown to 150. Its academic objective has been to train men at the graduate level for the paper industry, not necessarily research men, but men scientifically trained who have demonstrated their ability to perform the research function, who are acquainted with research technics, who recognize the rewards and hazards of research, who have been taught how research as a tool may economically be used in the service of society through the industry in which they are trained. Experience has demonstrated that these educational products rapidly become the junior training cadre of the individual companies employing them. These men become the bridge between scientific and research activities and the production needs of the industry. Percentage-wise, the academic product has been equally employed by the large and small company.

Thus the institute has demonstrated that very small and large segments of an industry alike could be provided with selected manpower, specifically trained, that all of the scientific literature pertaining to the industry could be made currently accessible, that specialists in the varying branches of science in whose realm the fundamental problems of the industry lie would be kept available, and that special scientific equipment not normally available to any individual company could economically be centralized. It has proved that such an institution combines a fundamental knowledge of the materials, processes, and products of the industry with an understanding of its current practices and, at the same time, supplies the objective approach without the necessity of expensive orientation of staff. It has made a definite contribution to the understanding of research on the part of management and the men being trained as its juniors. It has developed an appreciation of the part research can play in the service to society and, particularly, to that portion of society served by its industry, and it has contributed to a clearer vision of the widening horizons of the industry's bountiful markets, the needs for meeting new use requirements, and for the development of new products. Finally, we must appreciate the contribution the institution has made to the promotion of national security in the present war. It has served as a community reservoir for the accumulated research results and specialized technics of an industry where they could be piped to the various war agencies.

I believe that The Institute of Paper Chemistry has demonstrated that it stands as a symbol of a most productive partnership—education and industry—and affords definite proof of the opportunities opened through cooperation. It represents, I believe, the vision of an industry. It is an example of the tenacity of purpose necessary to the prosecution of research and the concentration of the resources and facilities which are needed to help an industry in its component parts to develop on all fronts men, products, and markets. It blazed the trail. Some other industries are following in the pattern it shaped. Others can, I sincerely believe, fruitfully achieve similar results in the same fashion.

THE GROWTH FACTOR IN

SMALL BUSINESS

IN OUR ZEAL for generalization and oversimplification we speak of small and large corporations and attempt to fit all industrial enterprises into one or the other category. Yet no criterion justifies a sharp line between these two groups, even though we can agree on the proper category for almost any one company. Among the criteria often applied is capitalization,* and here the twilight zone might be fixed as between one and five millions of dollars.

Given the question, how can small business serve itself and be served by industrial research and development, gross sales are a more useful figure for defining our subject. Size, however, affords no measure of the extent to which a company should

---

*Research — A National Resource: II — Industrial Research; December, 1940; National Resources Planning Board. The number of men employed is plotted against the various sizes of companies expressed in terms of net worth. Net worth is probably a better financial figure to gauge the size of a company by than capitalization. It is shown that 5 per cent of the men employed in research activity in this country are employed by companies having a tangible net worth up to $1,000,000; twenty-five per cent of those so employed fall in the bracket between $1,000,000 and $10,000,000. The remaining 70 per cent fall in the bracket between $10,000,000 and $1,000,-000,000. In that 70 per cent bracket the boundary line dividing it into two equal parts comes approximately at the $100,000,000 size.

support research, as both opportunity and necessity vary widely with different kinds of enterprise. The 1940 survey of the location and extent of industrial research activity in the United States shows clearly that although a substantial number of small and medium size corporations engage in research, their total effort is relatively small. The bulk of industrial research is supported by comparatively few large corporations.†

It is characteristic of smaller companies that their research activities are not set apart in a functional unit. The individual in charge of a company's research activities will have other administrative responsibilities; those engaged directly in the work itself may have other duties. The research activities of small companies tend naturally to be individualistic. Research may center in a close group of technically trained operating executives or in one inventive type of individual. These widely varying circumstances are a major factor in determining the relations of the professional research organization to small industrial enterprises.

There is some misunderstanding as to the size of a company which employs the services of the research consultant. While it is dangerous to generalize from one example, I venture the opinion that the situation of other research consultants is not unlike that of ours, whose clients are found largely among the medium size ($1–$10,000,000 capitalization) and the large corporations. By number, possibly 20 per cent of our clients are small companies, and from these we derive less than 5 per cent of our current income from professional services.

As recently pointed out by Fairfield E. Raymond*: "The small enterprise has the option of carrying on whatever sort of research it can afford, of developing its own technique, of

---

†*Ibid.*, Section IV.
Ibid., Section II, Page 79.

training its own technicians and experts, of acquiring new knowledge by hiring trained engineers or by participating in professional-society activities, by paying for the services of consultants or scientists, by financing specific research projects through technical institutions, or by buying outright new technical developments or inventions from individuals or other companies." A company must make a judicious choice among these several options. With changing conditions a company so situated would be expected to shift its policy from time to time as necessity dictates.

My own experience confirms Raymond's finding as to the intermittent and irregular use of the preceding resources. The reason is to be found in the limited means of the small company for the support of any sustained long-term research effort. While the percentage of gross sales spent by small concerns varies, quite widely according to recent surveys,* 2.5 per cent of gross sales appears to be an average figure. A conservative company adhering to the average and with a million dollar sales may be expected to have a research budget of $25,000 a year. In order that this budget may be used effectively the company must allocate a major part to immediate organizational expense, for, as pointed out in an earlier paper,† the services of a research consultant and related agencies are seriously handicapped if the client does not have on his own staff at least one individual competent to participate in the work and to see that the findings are intelligently and usefully applied.

It is becoming increasingly necessary for the small company to support a technical staff, and it is from these expenditures

---

Ibid., Section II, 8, page 124.
†"Management and Research Consultants" by Raymond Stevens and Earl P. Stevenson, *Chemical and Engineering News*, American Chemical Society, *21*, 1869, November 25, 1943.

that it may expect to receive the highest return. Such a group can participate with benefit in the activities of the scientific and technical societies related to the company's industry, in the use of technical data published by the technical and scientific societies and government laboratories, through contacts with educational institutions, and through the assistance of large industrial research organizations that are back of the materials used by the company. As a matter of fact such representatives of small industry are constantly calling upon the research consultant and thus availing themselves of the somewhat institutional position of such organizations. In other words, there is greater participation in the activities of small companies than would be indicated by the figures which I have cited in the case of one research organization.

Mention should be made at this point of the services rendered by individual consultants. As a group they may be more adaptable to the intermittent and informal relations required by small companies than are the larger engineering and research institutions. A few years ago the combined Engineering Societies of New England published a directory of "the New England research agencies, consulting services and colleges and universities available to New England's industrial, commercial and other interests for the solving of their problems by the practical application of the research method."* Over five hundred institutions and individuals are listed. This extensive list is indicative of the great reservoir of technical advisory and cooperative service available throughout the industrial section of the country, but all too little used by small business.

---

*Directory of New England Research and Engineering Societies, published by Engineering Societies of New England, Inc., in cooperation with the New England Council, May, 1939.

Technical Manpower Missing

How to make effective use of this reservoir has been accepted in New England as a challenge. In the fall of 1941 a plan was formulated to assist small industries in their use of research methods. The New England Council with its large membership among all sizes and kinds of businesses was the leader in this project. The situation of New England was surveyed under a committee headed by Dr. Karl T. Compton, President of Massachusetts Institute of Technology.† From this developed the New England Industrial Research Foundation, with its major purpose the promotion and utilization of research methods by New England industry, both large and small, but with the needs and problems of the latter a particular objective.

The main conclusions which I have drawn from my part in administering this foundation from its beginning are (1) that there is a widespread and intelligent interest in research by business executives in small companies, (2) that more funds are available than are being spent, (3) that opportunities for research and development are recognized, (4) that the missing element is in technical and scientific manpower. The program of the foundation can be implemented only by making men available to meet the needs of the progressive small business. In the absence of such help the foundation has largely curtailed its activities for the duration.

The office of the New England Industrial Research Foundation has received inquiries from other industrial areas, and I have no doubt that in the postwar period a number of organized centers facilitating the use of available research aid

---

†"Industrial Development in New England," an address prepared for delivery before the 75th Anniversary of the University of New Hampshire in the joint meeting of the New England Council and the American Association for the Advancement of Science at Durham, New Hampshire, on June 24, 1941.

will be established primarily for the benefit of the small manufacturer. Several states already have annual industrial conferences devoted to the application of research.

If I were asked to suggest specific steps that would aid small industry in the use of research in the immediate future, I would first discuss the matter of employment of men who speak the research men's language—men trained in our great technical educational institutions. It is not sufficient for the business executive to be sympathetic toward research; he must also have an understanding of its techniques and the ability to select the right kind of men.

It is evident from the record that large companies hire most of the technical men. Experience in this respect at the Massachusetts Institute of Technology is believed typical of the better technical schools; it shows that the large companies have studied the competition in their technical graduate supply market, and that they compete seriously and effectively for a continuing flow of young technical graduates into their organizations. Not so the small companies. Obviously, they have not recognized or realized the need, or have not studied the competition they must meet, for relatively they are not adequately represented in the technical graduate markets each year. It is not that they cannot meet the competition, for the small company appeals to many men merely because it is small, and the small company is much more flexible in the special salary or other conditions it can establish. The relatively few small companies that make a special effort to obtain technical graduates on a competitive basis have found no insurmountable difficulties.

It must be recognized, however, that the large industrial research organization has much to offer the young graduate: pleasant associations that continue earlier friendships, the opportunity to work in fields of specialized scientific interest, the glamour of belonging to a nationally known organization, the promise of early advancement with financial and social security. Also, in certain educational fields, notably chemistry and chemical engineering, the leading graduate schools have a definite vocational relationship with the established manpower requirements of the large industrial research organizations.

An analysis of the list of large companies that maintain the bulk of our research and hire the bulk of our technical men is most illuminating. A major portion of them are found to have started with technical development, to have been built on research and engineering. The names of the great companies with their great laboratories in the electrical, the petroleum, the chemical and process industries immediately suggest themselves. They do not hire technical men because they are large —they are large because they hired technical men when they were small and have kept on hiring technical men. By contrast the railroads, the coal industry, and other industries are large, but they are not relatively good markets for our technical graduates nor have they yet been relatively large supporters of research. The outstanding industries supporting research and hiring our technical graduates year after year are the chemical, petroleum, and electrical groups. The chemical and electrical industries grew from research and the use of technical men. The most spectacular increase in the employment of research personnel in industry in the period between 1927 and 1938, charted by Cooper, is in the petroleum industry. In that period the petroleum industry joined the ranks of those who knew how to use research wisely and generously—and as a result, the industry prospered greatly and the public profited enormously.

Many small companies, if they are to compete and assuredly if they are to grow, must learn first to compete for technical personnel. If competent technical personnel is intelligently absorbed and utilized, effective research will follow almost automatically. There are ample facilities available for advice, consultation, and direct and continuing assistance. Organized bodies, like that sponsored by the New England Council, exist or are being created to facilitate the use of such assistance. Most small companies are probably aware of the significance of research, but many of them are still unaware of the methods by which research can be utilized within their budgets and their organizational structure. The need now is not for more sources of assistance or free service—research breadlines. The need is rather for education of small company management in the advisability of employing technical personnel and in methods of utilizing research assistance now available. These needs, unfortunately, are still great; and in this area of society, ours is an economy of scarcity.

Clyde E. Williams

HOW THE

RESEARCH FOUNDATION

MAY SERVE SMALL BUSINESS

IT IS MOST FITTING to consider the question of "How Can Small Business Serve Itself and Be Served by Industrial Research and Development," on the occasion of the twenty-fifth anniversary of the central research organization of one of the nation's largest companies. It is a compliment to the foresight and splendid attitude of that company that it should provide this occasion for the consideration of this important problem. The Standard Oil Company (New Jersey) is one of the pioneers among the larger industrial organizations in establishing what are now known as central research departments. Although a few of the more research-minded corporations, such as American Telephone and Telegraph and General Electric, had central research departments before the last war, and several others had well-organized departments, the movement did not really get under way until Standard Oil and several other organizations, at the close of or shortly after the first World War, established highly organized central research departments, thus starting a trend which has gained impetus with the years. It is largely to these well-organized and effective central research departments that America and the world owe their debt for the outstanding production of war materiel that is bringing victory for the Allies. Thus, the first World War set the stage for industrial research in America, and the present World War made use of it for victory for America.

The Central Laboratory

The fact that the highly organized central research department is a creature of large industry does not mean that this useful tool is denied to small business. The principal requirements for the successful central research laboratory are suitable personnel, good management, and a well-equipped plant. The personnel should be not only well trained in the primary fields of interest but also expert in other fields so that they may give advice and consultation and direct activities in allied or fundamental fields of interest. The management should be so staffed as to be able to direct the technical phases of the research work and to keep it in productive channels. It should be cognizant of the commercial phases of the problems and hence able to plan and organize the research work and adapt it to commercial objectives. The management, also, should be in close touch with and sympathetic toward fundamental scientific research so that the correct scientific as well as practical atmosphere prevails in the organization. The research laboratory should have all the necessary equipment to enable the technical staff to carry on its work efficiently and with as much saving as possible in labor and time. Often, expensive equipment that is called for only occasionally represents a justifiable investment. It goes without saying that good library facilities with a librarian to look up and obtain references, prepare reviews of the literature, and perform other functions are essential. Other service departments such as a shop, analytical laboratory, instrument department, photographic laboratory, etc., are indispensable needs. Oftentimes, pilot plants of one sort or another must be operated. These require ample space, miscellaneous semi-plant scale equipment and the common utilities such as steam, compressed air, and gas.

The functions of the central research laboratory differ from those of the departmental or operating technical laboratory which, before the advent of the former, was largely responsible

Three Main Requirements

for the research work as well as technical control, trouble shooting, etc. The central laboratory does not replace the departmental or operating laboratory. Its problems are directed toward major changes in the company's products or processes and often the day-to-day changes in practice are left to the departmental laboratory.

Obviously, the operation of a central research laboratory of the nature briefly described above requires a substantial investment in plant and facilities and a large annual operating appropriation. Permanence of the operation is essential and constant growth is advisable for maintenance of good morale. The support of such an activity is not burdensome to the larger companies, many of which now spend from a few tenths of a per cent to several per cent of their gross income on research. For the small company, however, unless it is a highly profitable activity, the support of such a laboratory might prove burdensome. It can carry on its testing and control work, its trouble shooting, and a reasonable amount of plant research work financed from the operating account. However, for its forward-looking, new-product and new-process research, it must look toward the use of a large, highly organized central research laboratory like those available to the large companies as described above. This may be achieved through the sponsorship of research in well-established laboratories of research foundations and through membership in trade associations or other groups organized for the purpose of furthering technologic advancement in the industry.

The small business—if it is to function as advantageously from the technologic and research viewpoint as the large company, which not only operates a central research department but also may belong to trade associations and other cooperative groups which themselves engage in research and fact-finding pursuits—must have three main requirements satisfied: (1) It must have access to knowledge of the broad, technical status of its own and other industries, of new operating practices, new products and materials as they become available as the result of research and development by others, and of contributions currently being made to science generally. (2) It must make or have made for it appraisals of the types of research it should undertake or the direction which its business development should follow. (3) It must have access to the facilities of a highly organized research laboratory such as has been described above.

These conditions may be achieved through the sponsorship of research and development work in a research foundation which is operated for the purpose of giving this very type of service, and which is staffed and equipped to work in the particular field of research involved.

The research foundation, if properly organized and operated, can perform a research investigation for the sponsor, and give the same service as the large central laboratory can give its company on a given research or development project. The major difference is that the company-owned central laboratory works on numerous and varied problems for a single company, whereas the foundation laboratory works on a number of varied problems for a large number of different companies. The research foundation, if it is to serve *its* sponsor (the small company) as adequately as the central research department serves its company, must not restrict its services to laboratory research work. It also must provide the other functions listed in the paragraph above. That is, it must give the sponsor wise guidance in the selection, justification and planning of research investigations, it must direct the work so as to be of the greatest practical value, and it must be ready to change the course of its work as good business judgment may dictate.

The research foundation also should protect the sponsor

company's interests by retaining a proper consciousness of the value of invention and by assigning patents to the sponsor, by avoiding dissemination of the sponsor's trade information and details of research progress, and by being prepared to supply the proper publicity when it may be advantageous to the sponsor to do so.

In order to give this type of service, the research foundation laboratory should operate on such a scale that it can provide versatile personnel and the type of management and research facilities that are available in the central research laboratory of the large company. This means that the foundation laboratory either must be very large, and have a volume of business running into one or more million dollars a year, if its activities are spread over a number of fields, or it must be specialized in a relatively small field of activity and carry on a relatively large volume of work in this particular field. The research foundation should be so organized as to be able continually to add new equipment and facilities, and if it is a growing institution, new plant as well. It must also be prepared to conduct a sufficient program of fundamental research to maintain the proper scientific atmosphere and interest among its workers.

Companies experienced in industrial research know that patience, time, and money are needed to bring even a well-conceived project to a successful conclusion. Small business must not make the mistake of believing otherwise. Experience indicates, however, that important developments may result from research investigations carried on over a period of several years, at an expenditure of as little as $10,000 to $15,000 a year.

While the importance of good supervision of research work by the research foundation has been stressed here, it is equally important that the sponsor company have a man familiar with its operations and requirements to guide the work along useful channels. He should see to it that the laboratory submits frequent progress reports, and that occasional conferences are held among representatives of the company and of the research agency.

By following the procedures here outlined, the small business can engage in productive, original research on as satisfactory a basis as the large company with its central research establishment. To secure complete coverage in its research and technology, however, the small company, if possible, should maintain membership in a trade association or even in an informal group of companies engaged in the same type of activity. Such groups supply technical and economic information concerning the product, and they often conduct research investigations either in their own laboratories or in those of research foundations. This work is directed toward the development of new or extended uses or the standardization or improvement of the products or processes of common interest to the members. It usually does not involve an attempt to create new products or to develop novel processes. Such activities are best performed by the individual company.

The small business that cannot enjoy the benefits of securing information concerning technical products and operations through a trade organization must rely upon other agencies. It may often secure help from consulting and commercial research concerns, government bureaus, universities and research foundations. The research foundation is being called upon more and more to supply such information, not only to its sponsors but to the public generally. This is an important and an essential activity, which the research foundation must provide if it attempts to serve small business as the central research department serves the large company.

The major difference between big business and small business is one of history. The one has grown large because it is older, or has had more business acumen, or was more progres-

Opportunities Are Greater

sive. Small business is really young, potential big business. The reason that many small businesses became large is that their management undertook research and was successful not only in originating the new development and applying it commercially but also in protecting it under the U. S. patent system. Small business has the same opportunity for growth that big business had, only today the opportunities are greater. To survive and grow larger, small business must not only embrace research but it must protect its developments by patenting its inventions.

Thus, it is imperative that the research agency for small business be patent conscious and be able to transfer ownership of its discoveries and inventions to the company for which they were made. The numerous plans of government to serve small business will not be wholly successful because of this requirement. Its service will be largely like that rendered by technical trade associations or similar groups. No single company or group of companies is willing to risk the capital required to exploit a new process or product unless it can do so exclusively for a long enough time to profit by it.

It is apparent that the operators of research foundations, if they are to serve small business adequately, have a serious responsibility. It is essential that they give small business a sound appraisal of research problems and projects. It is highly important that a clear differentiation be made between research that is done for the purpose of training men or adding to the fund of scientific and technical knowledge on the one hand, and that designed to help industry solve a particular problem on the other. The plan discussed here is concerned only with research work that is expected to be directly profitable to the sponsor. If the purpose of the investigation is merely the development of scientific information which is for the benefit of science and not designed for the practical solution of the problem, the industrial sponsor should be informed that this is the case, and his support of such research should be made as a contribution to science and for the training of research personnel, and not as an expenditure for immediate benefit to his business.

Many research foundations have funds of their own for the support of fundamental research and they do not rely upon industry for support of such programs. Numerous universities have established or are establishing research foundations, engineering experiment stations, or some other form of organization designed to give the service described above for research foundations. The methods of operation of many of these vary from that described above. Some include as an essential purpose the training of men and the development of new knowledge. Practices as to assignment of patents, publication of results, etc., vary. Each serves a useful function and represents an activity that deserves the support of industry. In the intensified research program to follow the war, our most precious and critical resource will be well-trained research men. Our universities will do well to intensify and broaden their programs to include the training of men for research. And industry will do well to assist by the financial support of these programs. In this most essential activity, however, it is important that we do not lose sight of the product being sought, namely, trained research men. Establishment of fellowships for this purpose involves arrangements entirely different from those here described.

A. C. Fieldner

RESEARCH BY GOVERNMENT

AND ITS VALUE TO SMALL BUSINESS

In 1938, the Science Committee of the National Resources Committee, in a report on the relation of the federal government to research, stated that "From the earliest days of national history the government of the United States has conducted scientific investigations in order to establish a sound basis for its legislative and administrative activities. Governmental agencies were pioneers in this country in carrying on research.

"As the population has increased and new problems have arisen, such as those relating to agriculture, conservation of natural resources, and general economic conditions, the government has found it necessary to extend greatly the scope of its research program. It is now engaged in research on a vast scale."*

This committee estimated that the government spent about $120,000,000 on research during the fiscal year 1936-37, or 2 per cent of its budget. About a third went to agriculture, one-fifth to the armed services, one-tenth to the Department of the Interior, and one-tenth to the Department of Commerce.

Note: This paper was presented in Dr. Fieldner's absence by Dr. W. C. Schroeder of the U. S. Bureau of Mines. It is published by permission of the Director, Bureau of Mines, U. S. Department of the Interior.

*Research — A National Resource. 1 — Relation of the Federal Government to Research. November, 1938, p. 3. U. S. Government Printing Office, Washington, D. C.

The citation of sums now being spent for research is likely to give a distorted picture owing to war conditions and they hardly could be used as a basis of comparison. For example, a single agency such as the National Defense Research Committee, or one engaged in aeronautical research, might well spend the entire sum of $120,000,000 and much more.

Scientific and technologic research useful to business and the general public is conducted by the United States Department of Agriculture; the United States Department of the Interior, through the Geological Survey, the Bureau of Mines and the Fish and Wildlife Service; the United States Department of Commerce, through the National Bureau of Standards; the National Advisory Committee for Aeronautics; and the Federal Security Agency, through the Public Health Service.

Those are a few of the major agencies. As a matter of fact, there are about 125 different units of the government that are engaged in research.

In considering these 125 units, as well as the $120,000,000 that was spent for '36 and '37, it must be borne in mind that some of this money is spent for service agencies, as for example, the Weather Bureau, which collects and disseminates information on weather conditions, and the Census Bureau, which deals with statistics. A rather detailed analysis would be necessary to break this figure down between true research and other types of work. The $120,000,000 might be called a maximum figure.

Since the keynote of this Silver Anniversary Forum is the service to small business by research, I will concentrate upon such service from several of the above government scientific and technical agencies.

Research by the United States Department of Agriculture: The United States Department of Agriculture conducts more research than any other government department. Its work,

"Apple Honey" to Penicillin

coordinated by the Administrator of Agricultural Research, relates to the fundamental occupations of providing food, clothing, and much of the shelter that are necessary for human existence. These occupations and the host of small businesses based upon them are highly individualistic. They have little organized research of their own and depend largely on the service provided for them by federal and state governments through the Department of Agriculture and the state universities and experiment stations.

The Bureau of Agricultural and Industrial Chemistry conducts investigations and experiments in chemistry, physics, and other services to improve agriculture and develop new and wider industrial uses for agricultural products.

In connection with the rapid expansion of food preparation industries, the Bureau has given invaluable aid in the improvement of processes for the production of dehydrated meats, eggs, fruits, potatoes and other vegetables for the use of the armed forces of this nation and the allied countries. One of the regional laboratories, in cooperation with industry, led the way to the production of penicillin on a scale that promises to meet the needs for this important material. Another laboratory has developed a palatable syrup from apple juice, thus providing a new product to be manufactured by a number of small businesses. Of course, big business also benefits from many of these developments. Apple syrup is an example with which you no doubt are familiar under the name of "apple honey." Radio announcers have extolled the merits of apple honey for the proper conditioning of cigarette tobacco, and the manufacture of cigarettes, no doubt, is big rather than small business.

Other scientific bureaus of the department are the Bureau of Animal Industry, which functions as the central research agency for the livestock and poultry industries; the Bureau of Dairy Industry, which seeks to improve the milk-producing efficiency of dairy cows and the quality of dairy products; the Bureau of Entomology and Plant Quarantine, which is concerned with the insect enemies of crops and their control (this bureau developed the insecticidal uses of D.D.T. in this country, although it was first synthesized abroad); the Bureau of Plant Industry, Soils, and Agricultural Engineering, which investigates plants, soils, fertilizers, cropping methods, and engineering problems concerned with the production and handling of crops; and the Forest Service, which works on the conservation of forest growth and the better utilization of forest products.

United States Department of the Interior—Research on Mineral Resource Conservation and Utilization: Next to agriculture, mineral conservation and development are perhaps the most important fields for basic government research that have wide application to many of this country's industries and in particular to small companies that do not have research facilities of their own. Important research problems occur throughout the entire range of the mineral industries, from exploration, production, and preparation of crude mineral products to their final processing and utilization. The principal government agencies in this field are the Geological Survey and the Bureau of Mines in the United States Department of the Interior.

The Geological Survey is the largest contributor in the United States to geological science. It provides accurate topographical maps of the country, showing the location and nature of mineralized regions and thus providing the foundation for this country's mining industries. Geological information is required for many other purposes besides mining as, for example, in the construction of highways, bridges, and water storage projects. Its work also includes a comprehensive survey of the water resources of this nation and of Canada. Seasonal streamflow measurements over a period of years and determinations of the capacity and quality of underground water supplies have

•

been of great value not only for the development of municipal water supplies or irrigation projects but also in the selection of many sites for manufacturing or processing enterprises. The Federal Geological Survey cooperates with the state geological surveys in describing the geology of each state and coordinates these data in the national picture.

A short time before the outbreak of World War II, the Geological Survey and the Bureau of Mines began a joint program of exploration of domestic deposits of minerals considered of strategic importance in warfare but normally imported because of the low-grade or limited known reserves of the domestic deposits. Manganese, chromium, tungsten, nickel, tin, mercury, and antimony comprised the principal strategic minerals. Private industry could not be expected to bear the cost of exploring deposits which could not be worked at a profit when cheaper, higher-grade ores were available by importation. Neither could industry undertake at its own expense the development of concentration and beneficiation processes for these low-grade domestic ores. This work was done at public expense, much of it by the Bureau of Mines and the Geological Survey with subsequent publication of the results and procedures, so that these data have become available to all companies, both large and small.

According to its organic act, the Bureau of Mines is authorized by Congress "...to conduct inquiries and scientific and technologic investigations concerning mining and the preparation, treatment, and utilization of mineral substances, with a view to improving health conditions and safety, increasing efficiency, economic development and conserving resources through the prevention of waste in mining, quarrying, metallurgical and other mineral industries..." These objectives are accomplished in part by research in its own experiment stations and in the field and also by encouraging the research of others.

The bureau has served as a connecting link between research agencies as well as between producing and consuming interests. It is not responsible to any special group but owing to its status as an impartial organization, can render assistance in solving controversial problems of technology or giving advice on subjects in which the public interest is paramount.

Many large corporations are, of course, engaged in various branches of the mineral industries. In the aggregate they do a much larger volume of research than the government, and a number of corporations individually conduct much more research than the Bureau of Mines. That is as it should be. The nation's industrial advancement owes much to this large-scale use of research. The government has served a useful function as a pioneer in uncultivated fields and as an instructor of young workers who subsequently organized the industrial laboratories that followed. This function of the bureau was outstanding in the early days of the petroleum industry and was developed more recently in the coal industry, which is just getting under way in supporting modern research on improved methods of mining and preparation and on developing better equipment for the utilization of coal and its products.

As this work develops, Bureau of Mines research will be directed more and more toward fundamental conservation of the national fuel resources and the improvement of health conditions and safety in these industries, and basic problems in which the public interest is paramount. Present bureau projects that yield information widely useful to small industries are:

1. The survey of the chemical and physical properties of American coals, including tests for assessing their suitability for various uses such as combustion, carbonization, gasification, liquefaction, and the production of various chemical products.

2. Development of methods and equipment for increasing efficiency in utilizing coal as a fuel in small industrial plants.

3. Reduction of losses from spontaneous combustion and fires in coal mines and storage piles.

4. Investigation of evolution of inflammable or noxious gases from coal to improve ventilation in coal mines.

5. Study of mechanism of ignition and propagation of gas and dust explosions with a view to prevention or control.

6. Study of new methods of mining to increase recovery of coal and of methods of preparation that will reduce the loss of good coal in the refuse.

7. Research on the increase of safety in mining coal through the use of explosives and electrical equipment that will not ignite explosions and the development of means for reducing roof falls, which in themselves are responsible for a large share of accidents to coal miners.

8. Research on reduction of stream pollution from washery wastes and acid mine water through the development of practical methods for minimizing these wastes without imposing onerous costs on the industry.

Numerous publications giving the results of research or investigations relating to the projects that I have listed have been issued by the Bureau of Mines.* These are available to the general public and constitute a source of information for those who have no research facilities of their own—a situation that prevails in most units of the coal-producing and fuel-consuming industries.

Research on petroleum presents a radically different picture from research on coal. The twenty-fifth anniversary of the founding of the Standard Oil Development Company, which

*A. C. Fieldner, Alden H. Emery, and M. W. von Bernewitz, Bibliography of United States Bureau of Mines Investigations on Coal and Its Products 1910-35. Bureau of Mines Technical Paper 576, 1937, 145 pp.; ditto 1935-40. Bureau of Mines Technical Paper 639, 1942, 43 pp.

we are commemorating, is a striking example of the outstanding progress this industry has made in using scientific methods in the improvement of processes and products. Today the larger units of the petroleum industry have large research and development divisions staffed with some of our best scientists and engineers. Naturally the question arises as to whether there is anything for the government to do in petroleum and natural gas research. The answer is "yes." Much of the oil and gas is produced under highly competitive conditions by small operators who are not in a position to develop efficient methods for maximum recovery. The Bureau of Mines aims to supply this service for the national benefit of conserving an important resource.

The Geological Survey and the Bureau of Mines are deeply concerned with providing basic information on our petroleum reserves and the best methods for attaining maximum ultimate recovery. This includes research directed toward secondary recovery from fields that are approaching exhaustion. A few years ago the bureau established a field office and laboratory at Franklin, Pa., to aid the small operators in that district, where secondary recovery is under way. The data thus obtained are published and thus made generally available to all. As examples of other projects of general interest, the following studies may be cited: regional engineering surveys of oil and gas fields; reservoir characteristics of particular oil fields; methods of estimating oil and gas reserves (in cooperation with the Geological Survey); flow characteristics of oil and gas wells; analyses and characteristics of the typical crude oils of various fields; characteristics of gasolines sold in twenty market districts throughout the United States; disposal of oil-field brines and petroleum wastes; and certain phases of the chemistry of petroleum hydrocarbons. Even in these subjects the government has no monopoly on research but cooperates with industry wherever possible. However, the Bureau of Mines does conduct one monopolistic enterprise. I refer to the extraction of helium from natural gas. This work was greatly expanded during the war and at no time was this production inadequate to meet the demands of the Army and Navy.

Because of my greater contact with the investigations on mineral fuels, I fear that I have given undue attention to this phase of Bureau of Mines research. A large part of the bureau's work relates to the mining, beneficiation, and utilization of ores of the metals and nonmetallic minerals. Research on ore and mineral dressing has enabled small operators to increase recovery of high-grade concentrates from low-grade ores by applying better methods of gravity concentration and utilizing the constantly increasing variety of flotation reagents that have been discovered in the last two decades. Bureau metallurgists working in the various mining regions of the country also have been instrumental in adapting the more advanced practices of the metallurgical industry to the beneficiation of nonmetallic minerals and the washing of coal. Until recently these industries lagged behind in their technical methods. Such applications have been made to the preparation of ceramic clays, feldspar, bauxite, mica, talc, fluorspar, and other nonmetallics. These developments were especially valuable when it became necessary on account of the cutting off of foreign supplies to procure many of these materials in greater quantity from domestic sources.

United States Department of Commerce—National Bureau of Standards: The National Bureau of Standards, as its name suggests, covers a wide scientific and technologic field of research relating to standards and properties of various materials and manufactured products. This information is published and is very useful to large and small business and the public at large. It is an important agency in promoting the high standard of uniform quality for which American products are noted throughout the world. The bureau has taken a prominent part in developing instruments of precise measurement and uniformly reliable methods of measurement on a nation-wide scale.

Some idea of the diversified activities of this bureau is given in the papers appearing in its Journal of Research. Recent numbers have contained reports on such varied subjects as improved methods for controlling the composition of metals and alloys through the use of the spectrograph, the stability of different kinds of paper when exposed to light, the properties of steel columns made with perforated cover plates instead of lattice work, the properties of commercial masonry cements, the density of leather and its significance, and the characteristics of various hydrocarbons in petroleum.

To help business, especially small business, the bureau for some years has operated a research-associate plan. There are now over fifty research associates stationed at the bureau, representing fourteen industries. Most of these are studying fundamental problems, the solutions of which have wide applications. The Bureau of Mines also conducts research in cooperation with industrial groups or individual companies on problems in which there is a broad public interest usually connected with conservation of life or mineral resources. In such cooperative research the present policy is to require the transfer to the government of all patents arising from the work.

This thumbnail sketch is limited to the principal old-line research agencies of the government. I have not discussed some of the newer agencies that are growing rapidly, such as the National Advisory Committee for Aeronautics and the National Institute of Health of the Public Health Service.

Research: A Point of View

Nor have I mentioned the vitally important research of the Army and Navy, the National Defense Research Committee and the Office of Production Research and Development of the War Production Board. Their achievements are another story that will be told after peace is restored. Then some of their war developments will be turned to peacetime use just as swords were beaten into the plowshares of old.

Discussion: MOREHEAD PATTERSON

Dr. Lewis has asked me to represent small business and small business management and its attitude towards research. You will find it hard to believe that there are managements of successful small businesses who do not know what research is. They don't know the definition of it and they don't know the limitations of it, and they don't know the possibilities of it.

Their first, and natural, attempt is to apply practically to their own business what they have heard about research. I think all of you will admit that in applying research practically to your own business you have to cut down a great many of the generalities that are taught about research. Research, after all, is not a thing that you can buy and sell and cut off by the yard, as pointed out by one of the earlier participants in the Forum. So, when the small manufacturer tries to think how he can apply research practically to his own business, he finds that he doesn't understand what research is.

Let's take the position of a company such as my own. For many years we have been in the machinery business. For many years we have been successful in the machinery business. We have been so because our policy has been to develop bigger and better and finer machines practically every year continuously. Our business happens to be cigarette machinery, cigar machinery and bakery machinery. We have always spent a percentage of our sales dollar in developments to make our machines better and finer and mechanically more perfect and we are still in business.

The question is, "Is that research?" I don't think it is and I will tell you why. I think research is a point of view more than it is an actual fact. It is a habit of mind. It is a habit of approach to a practical problem. I don't think we have had it; at least we never had it until shortly before the war.

When your product development has followed along the same line for many years, you reach the stage of diminishing returns, where a dollar spent on development does not yield a dollar of real improvement. Your men reach the end of their development fertility. They can improve the setting of a bearing, they can improve a gear train, they can improve the appearance of the article, but when all is said and done, change becomes change for its own sake alone.

A few years ago, I felt that we had reached that point and that something must be done about it. So I went to M. I. T., where I thought they ought to know something about it, and I asked Dr. Bush, "What shall I do?"

He said, "Go down and see Nat Sage." I went down and talked to Nat Sage, and he listened very sympathetically to the problem and said, "Well, if you take an airplane from here to San Diego, and you throw something out the window at any point in the trip, you will hit a company about your size that has exactly your problem." I was greatly comforted by that.

I began to think about the problem a great deal. I went and talked to everybody I thought might know the answer, and I concluded that a research program was our solution. I came back and reported it to our management. Everybody looked at me and said, "Well, that is very interesting, fine. We are glad you are back. How was the trip?"

It was not that they were unsympathetic or uninterested, but that they, as busy men, had not thought through this new approach to their future problems.

So I think that the thing that could best be contributed by the research people of this country to small business would be some form of educational program, not preaching to management, but interesting management in the habit of mind of research men, creating a desire, a positive desire to find out the latest thing that is happening, something advanced, some new principle, some new habit of thought, particularly, which they can apply to their own future.

I think that the research mind is the most important thing of all to sell to the management. It is a new thing, not in point of years, but in point of application to the practical problems of small business.

I would suggest that somebody take on the hard problem of educating management.

I have a few suggestions here. If you could persuade one or more people in the management of a small company to go to M. I. T., we will say, or any well recognized engineering school, and sit down with men who do that kind of thinking all day long, and get acquainted with them, get to know them, get to know their habits of thought and how practical their thinking is, a great deal might be accomplished.

After all, management can not be expected to be intelligent in its selection of a research director and the approval of the projects he proposes until it has learned the language.

I am reminded of the fact that John Hancock at one time was investigating the Jewel Tea Company and that for three months he actually rode on the delivery wagons delivering tea to find out what the business was all about.

If you can get management to start riding the delivery

wagons of research, you will begin to get them to understand what it is all about. They think of it as test tubes now. They think of a chemist as a fellow who has had high school chemistry. They think of a research director as a man who pulls rabbits out of hats. They cannot see how this can be fitted practically to their problems. They tend to improvise from within, rather than to accept the new habit of thought and its trained exponents. I think the thing to do is to start them off by really educating them and if you can really educate them, then I think they will accept research as a practical part of their forward picture. It will be of great benefit to them and to the country.

Incidentally, if anyone in this gathering, or anyone at this table will attempt this program and work it out, I would like to be the first to get educated.

Discussion: FREDERICK W. WILLARD

Mr. Land has given what is to me a fresh viewpoint, a fresh procedure, and his enthusiasm is infectious. I hope to live long enough to see the fruition of some of his ideas. His comments concerning an infinite series of small monopolies interest me and presently I shall mention that topic again.

Mr. Steele presented a very instructive picture of a cooperative undertaking for a single industry. It represents perhaps one of the most outstanding successes in that field. There have been others. I think the National Canners Association has accomplished a great deal, but I think Mr. Steele's organization is really outstanding, and he has given us some very practical ideas.

Mr. Stevenson, out of the abundance of his experience, has shown us some of the hindrances, some of the problems that

inhibit the use of available facilities for research by the small
enterprise.

He has undertaken to discuss the definition of a small enterprise, at the same time admitting that nothing of that kind
can be arbitrary or positive at this stage. It may well be that
some day we shall need to have some sort of a practical definition.

To that end I take issue with one of his suggestions concerning a basis of definition, namely, the gross sales. At the
same time, I don't believe that the cost of sales is a satisfactory
basis. I would suggest for future consideration a figure representing the total cost of salaries and wages in the enterprise.

Mr. Williams has given us a very clear idea of a type of
institution which has been highly successful, and for which
we have greater need. The non-profit research institution is
certainly one of our best instrumentalities for the entrepreneur.
He has shown in some detail how it works, and it certainly
does work. If we may judge by the load which the two principal institutions of that kind were carrying prior to the war, we
can safely predict that the new Southern Research Institute
has a grand opportunity.

There is one point in connection with any of these cooperative enterprises for the use of the small industry which
I think we should seriously think about. It is my considered
opinion that an important, if not the most important, obstacle
in the way of development of cooperative research institutions
is the inhibitive effect of our federal statutory prohibitions
which hang like the sword of Damocles over the heads of the
cooperative undertakings of this character.

This situation is not new. One of the *mores* of the American people is to have a sort of allergy toward any group which
smells of monopoly.

Unless we are willing to face this problem realistically, not only will we continue to stifle new enterprise, but we will jeopardize our world position as an industrial nation. A policy such as we have followed in this country for the last five decades of burning down the house to smoke out the rats is a negative policy which bodes no good for us in the future. By following it we assume that we haven't the intelligence nor the collective will to control abuses of the principle of free initiative except by destroying the initiative.

Finally, I want to say a word for those great federal institutions which have served us so well in past years and are serving so well today. They have been a breeding ground for scientific men. Institutions that have given us a Waldemar Lindgren, a Harvey Wiley, are an asset that we must cherish.

I hope that we will not see as a result of the growing impatience directed against the recent proliferation of federal agencies, a choking of these great scientific bureaus which have served us so well. It behooves us as private citizens to do everything in our power to impress upon our legislative servants the great work that these institutions have done and the great work that they can do in the future. What they have done for small business enterprise in the past is not sufficiently well known, but it has been very great indeed. I say more power to them.

Discussion: JOHN W. ANDERSON

It seems in order that we touch upon three phases of the subjects discussed on this Forum by the distinguished participants. First, perhaps we should consider the relative position of small business and big business. Any efforts to treat small business as a thing distinctly apart from big business, or to attempt to fix a sharp line of demarcation between small business and big business, must reflect a lack of understanding of the basic character of our economy. Small business, like big business, is an integral and essential part of our great network of competitive enterprise.

Out of the growing capacities created within that network have come those goods and services upon which our people rely for progress in peace or for protection in war.

Big business could not exist without small business. Each breeds and feeds and needs the other. The nation needs both. Both need our patent system, unimpaired.

Our giant industries constantly draw heavily upon smaller manufacturing organizations for materials and components. Problems of management usually make impracticable any attempt on the part of a great corporation to monopolize all of the steps necessary to produce all component parts of its end products. This is particularly true of such products as motor vehicles, most of the component parts of which are supplied by smaller manufacturers. Some of the automobile manufacturers have at times attempted to produce a substantially larger percentage of the component parts of their vehicles. They have found there is a limit beyond which they cannot go profitably. There is a point beyond which coherency of controls cannot be maintained. There is a limit beyond which the smaller manufacturer, specializing in a particular type of components, through his concentrations inspired by his competition, can invent and produce better components at lower cost than can the vehicle manufacturer or his subsidiary.

Most of the component inventions which have made the motor vehicle the dependable marvel it is today have originated with smaller manufacturers or with free-lance inventors. Many hundreds of such unaffiliated manufacturers, for parts which they use in the manufacture of their components and assemblies, draw in their turn upon thousands of other manufacturers. Supporting our larger industries, in fact, are descending bracket after bracket of producers, the demands of which penetrate at last to all our basic industries and services.

I think we should keep in mind also the interdependence of big business and small business. Big business supports and can support tremendous research organizations. Small business in many instances supports small research organizations. In one small manufacturing business with which I am familiar there is a three-man research department. Out of that research department have come some interesting things of benefit to all Americans.

You all remember the jittery gasoline gauge, the one with the delirium tremens that wouldn't stand still. Well, a small research department cured that one. Out of that research department, three men, happily working together, developed the external windshield wiper equipment used exclusively on bombardiers' windows and on windshields of our fighting aircraft, a contribution of which any manufacturer could be proud.

In many other ways that small research department has contributed to the better living of a great many people, and there are thousands of similar organizations, small organizations in the United States, that provide the very seed-bed of industry in this country.

The large research organization has a capacity greatly beyond that of the small manufacturer's research department, for refinement, for pure research; but if you will examine carefully the actual creative record of industry, I think you will find that the creations, the inventions, on which we rely most today, more than out of large laboratories, certainly more than out of any cooperative laboratories or any governmental laboratories, have originated with the free-lance inventor and the small research department.

The ability to refine, for the market, some of those inventions, such as the synchromesh transmission—which came, I think, from a free-lance inventor—lies almost exclusively with the large manufacturer, such as Dr. Kettering's laboratory.

I will agree that there is a great deficiency among the small manufacturers in appreciation of what research is and what it means. I think a great deal of educational work can be done along that line.

When a previous participant in the Forum mentioned that fact I called to mind one instance where a rather large manufacturer of razors and razor blades had a great deal of trouble with its razor blades. It could not make a razor blade, apparently, that would stand up and give satisfaction to its public, and it was greatly concerned. I remember one day particularly when the sales manager of that company wept on my shoulder.

He said, "I go out and I build distribution and these rotten blades tear it down as fast as I can build it."

So they went to one of the outstanding commercial research organizations in the country to ask them what to do to make a good blade. I am mentioning this as a small manufacturer so that you may better understand the deficiency of some of our somewhat larger companies in the matter of research or engineering.

They posted their fee and the investigation started. It lasted a very short time. The engineers carefully but courteously explained to the manufacturer that all he had to do, instead of using strip with the grain parallel to the edge, was to turn it around, putting the grain at right angles to the edge. There was an example where a little bit of research would have done a corporation a lot of good. Those blades are good blades today.

One of the major strengths of our system of competitive enterprise is that it is essentially dynamic. There is no prescribed limit to the number of enterprises or to the growth of an individual enterprise. And there is no conceivable limit to the heights of creative and productive achievement to which our industrial civilization may rise except as those limitations are imposed by our own unenlightened proclivities.

Most of our great enterprises have had their small beginnings. All or nearly all were at one time small business. Each such small beginning is rooted in an idea born of a purpose inspired by a hope of reward. Out of such hopes have come that will to work, that ambition to create and to produce, which has kept America so far ahead of all world competition.

Small business has come to be understood for certain purposes as all those enterprises in America employing less than 500 people. I think we on this Forum have treated as small business some enterprises that employ a great deal more than 500 people. So the smallness of the business is of course relative. The Standard Oil Company and other large petroleum producers and refiners are admittedly big business. Compared with these, my business is small. But compared with very small businesses my business seems extremely large.

Small businesses number about three and a half million firms, being more than 98 per cent of all our business organization. Active in their management are more than 7,000,000 people. They furnish employment—I am speaking now of the small businesses employing 500 people and less—for 67 per cent of our wage earners. They produce 47 per cent of all our manufactured goods. Yes, small business in America does a big job indeed.

One struggle sapping our nation's strength today is an age-old struggle. Always there are industrious producers. Always there are others who choose not to produce, or to perform any service in support of a productive economy. Such non-producers choose rather to live, by force or by cunning, upon the wealth produced by others.

I think there is no group in America to whom that fact can be better emphasized than a group of research men such as we have here today. The very nature of their work makes research men addicts to truth and to honesty. It is difficult for them to conceive of the type of attacks that are being made today upon the very institutions that support their research and the industry which it serves.

Yes, some non-producers choose to live by force or by cunning upon the wealth produced by others. Therefore, those who create and produce must have for their creations the protection of just laws, or they become discouraged. They cease to try. Which brings to mind a recent amusing incident.

An amateur economist urged a practical industrialist to meet a certain professional economist whom the amateur admired. A quiet dinner was arranged. The industrialist listened attentively past midnight as the fervent student of thick books on human behavior and economic trends explained how he and his associates had delved for years, back through modern history and beyond, into the fragmentary ruins of departed civilizations. He explained it was his purpose to discover what it is that makes man click. When asked at last for comment, the man of industry suggested, as a possible short cut to the answer sought, that the economist attend some vaudeville show offering a trained seal act. He was asked to note that after each stunt, however slight, the seal is rewarded with a hunk of fish.

The economist was invited to go backstage after the performance and ask the trainer what happens when someone appropriates the supply of fish. He was told, no fish, no act. The performers lose interest and lie down.

The same thing happens when the businessman or laborer no longer smells, down his tough road, his appetizing hunk of fish.

The will to achieve and succeed must spring from sound incentives and from confidence in the certainty of reward.

Americans are all descendants of foreign families. We are the same kind of people they were. Why is it, therefore, that our industrial civilization in America has attained such commanding heights, beyond any of the recorded dreams of those who founded our republic?

The answer is clear. Those heights have been reached because our Constitution, and the laws which have sprung from it, have offered our citizens greater certainty of rewards for their contributions to public welfare than had been assured ever before to any people.

So, in behalf of all small business in America, as well as in the interest of all industry and all our people, let us urge that the inducements of our American way of open competitive enterprise be perpetuated. Let us urge that the related inducements of our patent system be most fervently protected by our Congress and by our courts. Then, to enhance all such incentive, let just laws, requiring fair play in open competition, be most diligently enforced.

We must put American business, both large and small, completely upon its own initiative again. We must restore the inducements of our inventive economy. We must release again the full potentials of open enterprise. Then let us boldly deny that history must repeat itself. Let us deny that fertile nations must eventually breed, out of the luxuries and leisures they at last create, the lunacies that lead to their destruction.

Discussion: T. G. DELBRIDGE

In 1920 the automobile people began to get worried as to whether or not they would have enough gasoline to run the automobiles that they planned to make. So they got together with the oil people and formed the Cooperative Fuel Research

Committee, which was supported jointly by the Society of Automotive Engineers and the American Petroleum Institute. Since that time the work of that committee has been most successful. Instead of abusing each other we get together and attempt to solve our mutual problems.

Two years ago the success in the fuel effort encouraged the formation of the Coordinating Research Council, sponsored jointly by the Society of Automotive Engineers and the American Petroleum Institute. During those two years several small business representatives have come into that group to make their contribution, and they are contributing not only technically in our research work, but also financially, because the budget this year for the Coordinating Research Council is $100,000, of which approximately $70,000 is contributed by the two sponsors, and the balance by folks who are interested in the research results.

The manner in which the petroleum industry has conducted its cooperative research is well worth while. We have been able to interest, to influence, and in some cases even to direct colleges and government bureaus. I predict that in the postwar years cooperative research as practiced by the petroleum industry will increase and will be adopted by others.

Finally, during twenty-five years of such cooperative work in the petroleum industry, the larger companies have contributed far more than their share, and among the leaders has been the Standard Oil Development Company.

Discussion: CHAIRMAN W. K. LEWIS

There are two points I should like to make. In the first place, I feel that there is an unsolved problem as to how to handle the research needs of small business, or at least one phase of those research needs, and that is the problem of competitive research in contradistinction to cooperative research. Cooperative research has been extraordinarily successful and has a large and important future ahead of it. By and large, there aren't many obvious rocks in the road.

By competitive research I mean the problems of small business which are vital to the life of that business, and the solution of which, if made available to his competitor, will seriously handicap the success of the businessman.

The need of small business for scientifically-trained men is extremely real. It means that our universities and technical schools have not met the problem that faces them. We must try to meet it in the years ahead. In doing that we need the co-operation of business, both small and big.

There is only one way in which men can be trained for the research phases of industry after they receive their broad technical training. They must be taught the research technique by being given research to do.

In the early phases of that training the work can be done in the university to best advantage. If it can't, it means that the university ought to be shaken down, reorganized, and made to do its job.

In the conduct of that research, research results are sure to accrue. That field, I feel, is the field which the university should occupy in conducting industrial research.

Progress has already been made in that field. In the institution with which I am associated we started at an early date and large numbers of great institutions have undertaken work successfully. That line of effort in the universities does open a splendid way of training the men that industry needs. We must develop that training, find new men, give them the inspiration, interest and background of scientific knowledge and technique, in order to meet the needs of not only large industry but small industry. We need more of those men than we ever surmised before.

Discussion: FRANK A. HOWARD

A great many of the speakers have paid their respects to those who would change our patent laws, and to those who would prosecute industry for the way it uses its patents. These difficulties in connection with patents have been building up for a long time. Perhaps some examination of their causes may be helpful.

Our patent laws are based on the British Statute of Monopolies of 1623. He who created a new industry or imported it into the Kingdom became entitled to a monopoly of it for a few years. The patent laws of the civilized world have been based upon this fundamental concept. But in the 320 years which have elapsed a great many things have happened to our economic system. At the present time we know that for every patent which creates a new industry, there are many patents which do nothing but advance an old industry. When you apply to a patent on the advancement of an old industry the simple concept of absolute monopoly, you are often in difficulty. Industry realizes that, and has been making the patent system work by applying to it the simple rule of "Live and let live."

I have never in my experience seen an instance in which one company operating in a basic industry endeavored to maintain a monopoly for itself of any very fundamental improvement in that industry. It was always willing to see that the bottle-necks of production were removed by making its improvement available on reasonable terms to its competitors. Industry has therefore been instinctively and consciously adapting the patent system to changing economic conditions by its licensing policies.

New industries, of course, are still being created, entirely new products being invented, and it is proper and often necessary that a monopoly be exercised in these cases, in accordance with the original purpose of the Statute of Monopolies. Very often a monopoly is absolutely the only condition under which a new industry, even a new gadget industry, can be put on its feet.

We therefore have the two extremes—the "Live and let live" policy of unrestricted general licensing, for important improvements in basic industries, and the maintenance of complete monopolies for new industries. Between these two extremes there is a zone in which restricted licensing has seemed to be the best solution of the economic and business problems involved, and it is in this zone that most of the difficulties have arisen. Business has sought to modify the economic rigidity of an absolute monopoly by granting restricted licenses under various conditions. Those responsible for the enforcement of the Anti-Trust Laws have tried, quite successfully in the main, to drive industry away from these compromises, and force it to one extreme or the other. I think both industry and the anti-trust people have displayed a little lack of understanding in their handling of the problems in this wide zone between the two extremes. This friction has certainly discouraged research.

There is one other patent problem. Just now too many courts do not like patents, and do not often sustain them. Experience shows that this is likely to be a temporary phase. There is nothing very fundamental about it, although the Patent Planning Commission recommends legislation which would correct some heresies that have crept into recent judicial reasoning on the validity of patents.

PART THREE

THEME

"What place should industrial research and development organizations allocate to future work directed primarily toward national security?"

Robert P. Patterson

NATIONAL DEFENSE
AND INDUSTRIAL RESEARCH

THERE IS A GREAT VOICE in the world today, the voice of science and technology. It is a voice heard since ancient times but never until today has it spoken with such authority, have its words been so filled with promise, has it been listened to with such hope. And in no country in the world does the voice speak as eloquently as in our own.

Science and technology have changed and are changing the lives of all men. Not a single aspect of our society but feels their advance. The things we make and use, the food we eat, the clothes we wear, the way we travel and communicate, the houses we build, the way we cure and prevent disease, the way we fight—and the way we shall win—have all been fashioned by science. Both war and peace move under the sign of research, discovery and invention.

We are drawing closer to the first stage of victory in a total war. A crushing defeat for Germany is not far off. We shall stay on the job, with our Allies, until we make victory complete by smashing the Japanese. While our thoughts and energies must still be devoted to these tasks, without stint or limit, second place in our thought and planning should be directed to the problems of the future. How shall we repair the ravages of war? How shall we create a society in which full production and full employment can be maintained? How shall we promote and maintain the security of our country—and thereby

Problems of the Future

contribute to the peace of the world—so that no aggressor will dare again to jeopardize our status as a free people? The following remarks are devoted to the last question, on the part which science in industry can play by developing our resources and advancing our technology in the interest of national security.

If I now refer somewhat broadly to national security, it is not only that I conceive the term to embrace a wider field than the maintenance of an adequate army, along with the development of powerful and effective weapons, but also because in working on the normal products of peace we at the same time make an essential contribution to our military strength. First, then, let me briefly consider national security in its wider sense.

The highest goal of science is the welfare of human beings. No group such as that at this Forum, representing the laboratories and research institutes of industry, the universities, and Government—needs lessons from anyone on that score. No group is more clearly aware of what science has to offer in new products, new jobs, improvement in our standard of living. And no group will better realize the degree to which these factors promise economic stability and enduring peace.

It is to the interest of all that America's scientists engaged upon both pure and applied research should turn our swords into ploughshares as successfully as they have turned our ploughshares into swords. We shall need the development of new airplanes and helicopters, light metals and plastics, television and radio, new foods and medicines as much as we have needed and still need combat aircraft and jet propulsion, heavy armor and new explosives, radar and walkie-talkies, high-calorie rations, penicillin and blood plasma. I do not doubt that after victory we shall need the products of peace even more, for ours is not an aggressor country with imperialistic aims: the ideals of our nationalism are the ideals of peace and security.

To get the most out of all science, whether devoted to peace or war, there are certain things to be kept in mind. For one thing, research and development in industry, as in the university, flourish best in an atmosphere of complete freedom; control will wither science by destroying its precious essence of originality and spontaneity. If I were to add to the four freedoms of the Atlantic Charter, I might suggest a fifth freedom of inquiry, experiment and research.

With that principle in the forefront of our thought, I think we must concede that in view of its position in the modern industrial state, in view of the way science is woven into the cloth of our society, it cannot be left unorganized and unsupported save by sporadic benefactions. A few of the great industries of our country have been able to establish magnificent laboratories, and the discoveries and inventions flowing from them in a ceaseless stream have enriched our lives in peace and contributed heavily to our ultimate victory in this war. The laboratories of our universities, especially in the field of pure science, have steadily broadened and deepened the foundations on which all applied science must rest. The laboratories of our federal government, in the fields of agriculture, public health, medicine, meteorology, and the development of the tools of war, have also made an enviable record.

You will agree with me, I am sure, that essential as these contributions have been, we cannot afford to look exclusively to the laboratories and workshops of our major industries, universities and the federal government. While important scientific advances are not often made in attic, cellar or barn, as they were not so long ago, we must not permit the precious stream of discovery flowing from smaller industry and smaller educational institutions to be dammed up by neglect. Small business needs technical information; universities not possessed of vast endowments need help; scientific research and development are of national interest; and whether they be devoted to national defense, public health, public housing or to normal scientific activity for commercial purposes, they must be encouraged and if they need help they must have it.

Dr. Conant in a recent address said that the future of the physical sciences depended on the "number of really first class men" that can be turned out by our educational institutions. He urged that talented young men and women be afforded unhampered opportunity for research in both industrial and university laboratories; he advocated federal scholarships for high school graduates of technological promise, thus creating what he called "a scientific reserve" for national security. Without considering the exact means required to assure educational opportunities for young men and women of scientific promise, I am in full agreement with Dr. Conant's view as to the need and urgency. It is a problem which concerns all of you, and the nation must have the benefit of your constructive thought.

Certain aspects of research, apart from the development of weapons, must, it seems to me, continue to receive federal support or be carried on by the federal government. Agriculture, public health, public housing fall in those categories. Certain economic problems also are in need of the clear light of science. The federal government, with unique access to full statistical data on population, manufacturing, crops, markets, methods of distribution, is in a position to help shed that light.

Nothing I have said should be construed to mean that in any of these fields the activities of the federal government should preclude or foreclose the research and development of private industry or the universities. In normal research and development during peace, the larger share must be contributed by the citizens and not by their government. That is compatible with the view that in certain types of research the federal government must serve the needs of science. It must act as a stimulat-

ing force, it must furnish scientific information, it must lend
financial support if it be needed.

In many scientific inquiries there is room for a coordination
of effort. If it be deemed wise, the federal government might
be called upon to participate in that function. There is urgent
need for the fullest possible exchange of information between
scientific workers in industry, academic centers and the federal
government. How to achieve that coordination and a free exchange of data is a basic problem which has not been thought
through to a satisfactory conclusion, although much work
has been done upon it. On this too, the country needs your
judgment.

If I may sum up, the job of normal peacetime research is a
private job, not a government job. Those branches in which
the government will continue in the principal role are well
known; in no way do they conflict with the scientific functions of industry or university. What the government may do,
if it is called upon, is to furnish information and financial support. It may offer counsel, even leadership. It must not, in the
normal researches of peace, assume control.

Up to this point I have been dealing largely with scientific
and technological research which, though of major importance in the national interest, will go on with or without any
further plans we may make. But their advance will be facili-
tated if the factors to which I have briefly alluded are recognized and met.

Research and development devoted to the weapons, tools
and techniques of war present us with a tougher problem. Such
research will not go on to the extent required for our national
security unless support, guidance, even control, emanate from
central mechanisms. There is little I can say on this subject unless you will indulge my frankness and honest opinion.

In time of war, when the nation's existence is in danger, no body of men responds more generously, with greater energy and zeal to the needs of their country than our scientists and technicians. That was our experience in the first World War; it is also our experience today. Industries and universities have turned their laboratories and their test tubes inside out to give their country what it needed, whether they were summoned or not. Men and women who people those laboratories and wield the test tubes have given us more than we dared hope for. Thousands of lives of our fighting men have been spared, most of the wounded restored to health. I might say at this point that we are recovering for active duty for the army more than 50 per cent of the men wounded. Of course, that by no means includes the number of men that are totally restored to health. Our troops have been equipped with weapons equalling or surpassing those of the enemy; final victory has been brought immeasurably closer as a result of the efforts of our scientists and technicians.

With all our grumbling, good natured or otherwise, the fact is that on the home front we have scarcely felt the war, and that too is in large part to be ascribed to the efforts of our scientific workers.

But when peace comes, ours being a peace-minded nation, we shall have the greatest difficulty in keeping even a small portion of our best scientific brains on the job of maintaining the weapons of our armed forces at the high peak of effectiveness they now occupy. Unless a suitable program is evolved to draw and hold scientists of the highest level, they will not be available for government service in peacetime to supply the armed forces with the best science has to offer. They will return, as is only natural, to the industrial laboratories and the universities they came from. Nor will it be possible in the government laboratories that will be continued in peace to carry through all the research in ordnance, aviation, radar, rockets and new weapons, in the many specialized nutritional, physiological and other fields which underlie the waging of modern total war. The research facilities and the scientific manpower prerequisite to these activities will simply not be available to the government in sufficient degree. No acts of Congress or of the executive branch of our federal government can alone meet this deficiency. At almost every point of maintaining the technological strength of our armed forces—whatever mechanism we devise to achieve this end—we shall have to turn to the research laboratories and the research workers of industry and the universities to fulfill our needs.

To some extent, as I mentioned at the outset, our task is made easier—paradoxically, I may say—because modern war is total war. In other words, much of the research carried on by industry and universities to meet the needs of peace will meet the needs of war if this tragedy should be thrust upon us again. In the field of chemicals, rubber, synthetic gas, electrical instruments, engineering products, medicines, light and heavy metals, and food products, research for peace is research for national security. Also in the case of certain end-products of purely military use, the intermediary products may be suitable for civilian consumption.

Research and development in connection with most weapons are in a unique category. A host of factors stand as obstacles where the help of industry and the universities is concerned. Among these are the specialized tools and machinery required, the extensive proving grounds and test plants, the heavy expense, considerations of secrecy, the tenuous and inadequate liaison, during peace, between private industry and the armed services, the indifference or hostility of public opinion towards the development of war weapons in times of peace, the competing demands for commercial products.

Aware of the gravity of this problem and anxious to find at

least a partial solution, some of the leading scientists of the National Academy of Sciences, the National Research Council, the Office of Scientific Research and Development and members of the services engaged upon research and development have for some time past been weighing the merits of alternative plans for an organization which in the postwar world will deal with military scientific research and attempt to assure to the armed forces the scientific help and interest required of industry and the universities. In this distinguished audience there are several who have participated in these deliberations. I shall not burden you with detail, but I should like to mention briefly some of the questions which this group has had before it and to enumerate them for you so that we may gain the advantage of your thought. I do this more readily because I believe you will find that these questions are in almost all respects similar to those which industry must answer in developing its policies for research and development pointed towards national security.

The first question is how shall we obtain for the federal government the full time or consulting services of scientists on the highest level.

It has been suggested that we need an agency, with distinguished leadership, such as we now have in the Office of Scientific Research and Development, and with ample funds, to promote precisely those branches of research and development which will effectively contribute to our military strength. For this is the type of research which if left unattended and unsupported cannot flourish. Between the first World War and this war the funds made available for research and development in the military sphere were wholly inadequate. They are adequate now, but they must be kept so. The adequacy of federal appropriations to promote military research will determine, in large measure, the contribution that can be asked of private enterprise in terms of personnel and laboratory facilities. While the arguments for the creation of the new agency are impressive, I do not believe that such an agency would fully solve our problem. For the problem is essentially one of men and women, not of organizations. We must have sincere and spontaneous interest in research pointed to national security, and this does not grow out of organizations and subsidies alone, however important these may be.

An important obstacle in enlisting the aid of industry is the difficulty of liaison and interchange between the military services and industry. How can we best meet that problem, recognizing that there is one sphere fully and properly under military control, another fully and properly under private control, but with a large area of both spheres common to both? It is manifest that if industry's help in weapon development is needed, so far as the work requires, the military must take industry into their confidence, and vice versa. There must be an avenue between industry, university laboratories, government laboratories and the services, and there must be no one-way signs upon it. How can we best achieve this end, not theoretically, not in a plan, not in an elegant paper document, but in day to day shirt-sleeve work?

How shall extensive work in weapon development be financed? To this there is no simple and pat answer. No industry, however large, can be expected without government subsidy to undertake elaborate research for the weapons of war, especially the accelerated and ceaseless research peculiarly required in this field. How shall this subsidy be administered? What is its probable magnitude over the next 10 or 20 years? Perhaps I am asking questions that only a crystal gazer can answer; but I have confidence in the judgment of industry and of our scientists, and I would rather have your guesses than another's statistics.

Financing by way of subsidy or contract payments will, I

recognize, often not be enough. We shall need other forms of incentive, financial in character or otherwise. Over and above that, we shall need the approval, the sympathy, the leadership from civilian as well as military circles to enlist public opinion in support of a sound program.

I know that the exchange of patents and licenses in connection with research on military products is many-sided and troublesome. I mention it also because of its particular concern to industry. I believe, however, that a solution for that question will not be difficult to find, once a basic framework for the entire research and development program in the postwar world is erected.

What research facilities can and should the government provide for industry and universities? We cannot expect that the research facilities of the federal government will be increased after the war is over. We cannot expect, on the other hand, that even the largest industries will be able to provide the proving grounds and more especially the test plants, so that we can convert the successful solution of laboratory problems to successful solutions in production. Proving grounds will doubtless be made available to industry. What of pilot plants? These questions are, of course, intimately related with the problem as to what research functions in the development of weapons the federal government itself ought to continue to perform.

Planning for the results of science is unwise, for results cannot be anticipated. But we must not forego plans for research and suggestions in definite fields in which valuable results may reasonably be anticipated.

My friends who are scientists tell me that so rich and limitless, so untapped are the possibilities of science that the discipline of planning consists as much in saying what roads ought *not* to be followed as what roads ought to be. At every stage of developing our research on weapons we must have a stand-

Science Leads Tactics

ard of values, so that although research would not be confined, lesser problems would be subordinated to questions of vital national need. That standard of values must be keyed to the current strategic thoughts of our military leaders and must be accessible to the leaders of research. If the link fails in either respect, we cannot expect to gain the full benefit of our vast research machinery. Repeatedly this war has shown that science leads tactics; this will be fully as true in wars of the future. We will make our plans to suit our weapons, rather than our weapons to suit our plans.

The War Department has grown increasingly aware of the need for research and development in connection with new weapons. In partial response to that need there was created within the War Department, more than a year ago, The New Developments Division. This division is charged with functions relating to the initiation and coordination of research and development and the expeditious application of new weapons, devices and techniques. It has proved its usefulness and will, I hope, continue to do so in increasing measure. Its working relationship with the two scientific agencies to which we all owe so much, the National Research Council and the Office of Scientific Research and Development, has at all times been close and effective. I realize that this division marks only the beginning on the road to our goal. For in every one of its activities, after the war as now, the War Department must train its men, shape its plans and its actions so as to reflect the most recent advances of science. It must not lose sight of the fact that significant discoveries and inventions are usually the matured products of years of thought and experiment, with innumerable disappointments and failures along the way. There is no four-lane highway to scientific achievement; a bulldozer is needed every inch of the way.

In my judgment a single unified defense agency combining

Unified Defense Agency

the Army and Navy would go far towards solving many of the problems to which I have referred. The establishment of a corps of scientifically trained officers, for which persuasive arguments have been offered, is only one step, of many, which the creation of a unified defense agency would facilitate. It is a step which merits serious attention, whether or not a peacetime scientific agency, of the kind I mentioned before, is created. It envisages the training of a group of talented young scientists, and others with professional skills, within the existing framework of the armed forces, as an integral part of the Army and Navy. Members of this group would have their regular basic military training at the academies. Once their talents were demonstrated, they would be given full opportunity to keep pace with the advance of science by post graduate work in universities and industry. They would be assigned to the research and development branches of the several services in accordance with proved ability. They would grow within the services, be acquainted with their problems and contribute not only in terms of professional skill, not only in propagating the views of science, but in linking the scientific and technical activities in universities and industry with the parallel activities of the armed services. This is a concept that commends itself to our attention; it is one on which the War Department is most anxious to hear the views and criticisms of industry.

I cannot leave these points without mentioning again the matter of science in education which I referred to before. The future does not belong to us. It belongs to our children and to their children. We must look to them for the future of science. Unless we give them the training, the opportunities, the facilities for turning their talents and their genius into a powerful and disciplined machine, we cannot envisage a bright future for science in America.

I think I have overtaxed your patience, and yet I have left

For Maintaining Peace

many points uncovered. You will also find fault with me, quite properly, I suspect, because instead of answering questions, as I was supposed to, I merely asked them. But I think in your lenience you will concede that the asking of questions, the raising of issues, is often as profitable as the giving of answers. I am sure that my questions are more profitable and worth more than my answers. I know of no group as well qualified to answer the questions I have raised as this group. I know of no group which will devote itself to that task with more energy, high purpose and sincerity.

It is a heavy assignment of responsibility to say that the future of our country in peace and in war is to a great extent in the hands of American scientists in industry, in schools, in universities and government. But I believe the responsibility is properly assigned, and I have confidence it will be met. Vice President Wallace once stated that science and technology, like good will, have no natural boundaries. The opportunities, the freedom, the security which science can give to our people can be extended to the corners of the earth. By so extending them industry will make its greatest contribution to national security. The perils of war give the precepts of peace. With the help of science and the men and women who make it we shall maintain that peace.

Discussion: R. E. GILLMOR

First I wish to state, with the utmost sincerity, that in my thirty-five years of observation and study of technical progress in the military services, and of the policies and programs underlying and supporting that progress, I have never encountered such a far-sighted, clear, fundamental exposition of guiding principles as those given in Mr. Patterson's paper.

Point of Vulnerability

Peace is going to come to us again and we hope soon, and we hope also that it will endure for a long time. But those of us who are in positions of social responsibility in industry or in government must remember that peace is largely a state of mind of a victorious people who are one of the nations that hold the so-called balance of power and who have every interest in maintaining peace.

We must also remember that as peace endures there is a growing tendency to believe that it is the normal state of affairs in the world, and there is a growing tendency to disbelieve that any nation would ever want to interrupt that peace. It is when that point is reached in a peaceful nation that it is at its most dangerous and vulnerable point, because then it is likely to receive a sudden blow from a nation that does not share that point of view, a nation that feels it is frustrated, a nation that will profit by war, or a nation that has been seized with some fanatical idea which drives it to form some sort of crusade in the world to force its views on other people. And it will seize a moment to strike when nations that it has to contend with are most vulnerable and most unsuspecting.

Twice in this generation we have gone right up to the brink of war disbelieving that it would ever occur. But still war struck. And in 1941 it struck as a lightning war, a lightning war which nearly succeeded and would have succeeded with a little better planning and a little more thorough preparation. It would have succeeded because of the development of lightning weapons, developments that had taken place in the preceding twenty years.

The development of weapons, as we engineers all know, proceeds from the general availability of scientific knowledge, an availability that is world-wide, and is distributed through media that are world-wide, such as scientific papers, and publications of various sorts.

In the next world war, which will inevitably come some day, but we hope not in our lifetimes, the lightning war will be much more feasible, because of the rapid development that is taking place and that cannot be stopped, and that will be world-wide. The only safeguard against it by a free and peaceful people such as ourselves is to be so far ahead in our progress that no nation will take the risk of attacking us. That becomes the responsibility, as Secretary Patterson has pointed out, of the entire population, and especially of the engineers, the scientists and the research workers in the universities and in industry and in the military services.

Secretary Patterson has answered all questions of fundamental principle that I can think of in his address, but he has propounded to us an extremely difficult but very important question which we are going to have to take a long time to answer. That question is, what means, what specific *modus operandi*, must be devised to insure the continuance of scientific and enduring cooperation between the military services and the laboratories and research organizations of the industries and the universities?

Discussion: REAR ADMIRAL J. A. FURER

It was particularly stimulating to me to be made aware at this Forum of the breadth and depth of the scientific thinking that is going on in the United States. In the War and Navy Departments we are very much preoccupied with finding a way of perpetuating in some manner the participation of civilian scientists in the military research that has been going on during the past four years. It goes without saying that the country, and Congress as representing the country, expects the Army and the Navy to take the major responsibility for the continued improvement and development of weapons and other instrumentalities of war in times of peace, because that is one reason for having a professional Army and Navy.

However, the last four years have demonstrated that civilian scientists can contribute in an outstanding way to the invention, development and operation of all manner of instrumentalities of war. In other words, that it doesn't require a professional employee of the Army or the Navy, whether civilian or officer, to contribute to national preparedness by assisting the armed services in solving their innumerable war problems.

We know, of course, that the government cannot continue to employ all of the scientists who joined the Office of Scientific Research and Development and the government laboratories during the war. In fact, most of them would not care to continue in that kind of research. Their interests normally lie along other lines. But we hope that some way can be found of retaining the interest of civilian scientists of the highest level in military research, not as full-time workers, but as planners, consultants and collaborators.

The government must really get a free ride so far as the thinking and collaboration of the leaders in science are concerned because there is no way of employing these men fulltime, or even part-time, and paying them adequately for their services.

A plan is under consideration for bringing together on a permanent board the principal officers of the War and the Navy Departments who have responsibilities for research, with representative civilian scientists from the various fields of science that are involved in modern warfare—the activities of the board to be managed by a small executive committee. This board would be the device for keeping science, as represented by the academic and industrial laboratories, in touch with and interested in the needs of the Army and the Navy. We have an example in the National Advisory Committee for Aeronautics of such a mechanism which has done an outstanding job for the Army and Navy for almost thirty years in assisting the services with the scientific problems of flight. Such a board must, of course, have funds of its own for conducting long-range research or fundamental research which may be of interest to all, but not the special business of any one of the technical services of the Army or the Navy. The money for the development and improvement of specific weapons must remain under the control of the technical services and bureaus of the War and Navy Departments which now have legal cognizance of such materiel. Just how much money should be appropriated for a board making long-range explorations is a figure which cannot be predicted in any detail just now. It is certain, however, that more money should be spent for research during the postwar peace period than was spent during the prewar peace period. For the fiscal year of 1940, that is for the year ending July 1, 1940, the Army, the Navy, and the National Advisory Committee for Aeronautics spent approximately twenty-five million dollars for research. That was the year before we got into the war, but when Europe had already been at war for a year and the war in China had been going on for several years. The amount seems a very small one when we consider that for the fiscal year 1943 the Army, the Navy, the NACA, and the Office of Scientific Research and Development spent approximately five hundred million dollars for research. In other words, twenty times as much as during the year preceding our entry into the war. Possibly some of the half billion dollars was spent for crash programs that were really in the nature of production, but it is not far from the truth to say that the half billion dollars were spent for research and development of all kinds of instrumentalities of war. I do not say that we need to spend half a billion dollars a year for research in times of peace, but it is certain that only twenty-five million dollars a year for research is not enough.

It is important that in times of peace the armed services should keep the targets for research up-to-date and show imagination in thinking of new targets. The fighting branches of the Army and Navy are the customers of the research laboratories. Closer liaison between those who plan the strategy for war and who are to use the weapons, and those who are engaged in research for the development of the weapons must be maintained. A considerable amount of revision in the thinking of the planners of strategy and tactics is indicated as necessary to get the most out of the liaison between these two groups.

A board such as I have mentioned for keeping civilian scientists interested in the problems of the Army and Navy and for collaborating with the services in the broad fields of research should not operate its own laboratories because this would lead inevitably to narrowing the interests of the board. It should do its work by contracting for the services of competent individuals and the best suited industrial and academic research institutions. In this way, the board will be able to avail itself of all of the most progressive and the most outstanding talent in the scientific research field. The Army and Navy must, of course, continue to operate their own laboratories as these form part of the machinery which they need for doing their work. We hope that the personnel for manning the scientific research institutions of the United States will not have received too great a setback due to the interruption during the war years of the education of scientists. The problem of how to stimulate the education of new generations of scientists is one that should be given serious consideration by such a board.

Perhaps I have not made myself clear as to the meaning of

long-range projects in speaking of the principal function of
the board which I have mentioned. It is difficult in any case
to define just what is meant by long-range programs as compared to short-range projects. An illustration may be of interest although it is a highly hypothetical one. The great expansion in the immediate field of operations of modern war
has come about largely because the greatest defense against
an adversary is distance—whether that adversary is an individual or a group of individuals as represented by armies or
fleets. That fact has resulted throughout the centuries in a
constant increase in the range of weapons. In order to keep
in touch with the adversary, man has found it necessary to
increase the range of two of his senses: namely, the senses of
hearing and of sight, particularly the latter. Innumerable inventions have been made to bring this about. Radar, for example, is an invention which is useful particularly because it
has increased the range and acuity of man's sense of sight. Let
us suppose some future discovery still further extends the range
of man's senses, particularly the three senses which the creatures in the animal kingdom, other than man, use so extensively
in their struggle for existence, namely, the senses of taste,
touch and smell. An enormous vista for research might be
opened up thereby, leading perhaps to the development of
new weapons of warfare. While it doesn't seem likely that
in warfare man will ever use to any extent the three senses
which I have just mentioned, it would be a bold man indeed
who challenged the possibility of their use.

We can be quite certain that weapons will be used in the
next war which have not been used in this war. All wars in the
past have started with the weapons of the last war. Although
in modern times new weapons have been developed during
the course of wars, usually they have not been exploited to
their full possibility during the war of their origin. During

World War I the submarine and the airplane, which had not been used in former wars, came into use although they had been invented before the war. The tank and chemical warfare came into use toward the end of that war, but that is about the sum of the new weapons which made their appearance during World War I. Not all of the weapons developed during World War II have yet been made known to the public but it is almost certain that some of them will be outmoded by the next war. Our major problem is to be ready with new weapons for the next war and to be in position to produce these new weapons promptly when threatened by the next emergency. This would appear to be a wiser course than to depend on the retention of large quantities of war material of all kinds remaining over from this war. This means that after this war we must spend much more money on research and development than we have spent during the peace eras in the past. We need your cooperation, good will, and interest to spend this money wisely.

Discussion: MERVIN J. KELLY

Knowledge gained from experience is probably the most trustworthy. In our consideration of the postwar relationships of science and applied science to the development of instruments of war we can probably obtain worthwhile bench marks by an appraisal of the relationships in these three areas that existed in the period before our country began its active preparations for war and in the early period of active preparation. I have had the good fortune to be closely associated with the research and development programs of our country in a number of the areas of instruments of war beginning in 1937 and 1938 when our Army and Navy first initiated the contacts with industrial laboratories on the instruments of war problems in the secret categories. If we look at the situation then existing in some of these areas, we may well arrive at conclusions that will be helpful in consideration of the organization of this type of effort in the postwar interval. I shall select a couple of areas of instruments of war research and development which rather well illustrate the two extremes of preparedness that resulted from the organization of, or perhaps better the lack of organization of, national effort in the instruments of war programs.

In the first of these areas, which will not be named, the laboratories of the military establishments, even with the small amount of money that was available for their work, did some rather far-seeing work in the thirties. During the years prior to 1938 they had applied to their instrument of war problems some of the most recent knowledge and discoveries of our pure and applied science laboratories. Even with limited funds, they had through a period of several years evolved the rudimentary tools and done the pioneering experiments that formed the basis of a rapidly expanding and highly important sector of new instruments of war development. I have nothing but praise for the initiative displayed and imaginative work done by these military laboratories during this period when their work was so completely secret that in carrying it out they were isolated from the pure science and industrial laboratories.

Since they were not in a position to discuss their problem and to enlist the aid of the scientists of our university and industrial laboratories, they had to work with the electronic and electromechanical devices and gadgets that the industrial laboratories made available for the peacetime needs of our country. Both because of the limitation of funds and the restrictions resulting from secrecy, their progress was slow, and little more than the surface was scratched in an area which was destined to be one of the most important areas of instruments of war. However, if the scientists and engineers of the military laboratories concerned had not been men of imagination and competence in development, we would not have had such a splendid foundation upon which to build expanding programs when the curtain of secrecy began to lift in 1938.

In 1938, a few industrial laboratories were told about the work of these military laboratories. Their aid was solicited in the expansion of the technology upon which these military laboratories had worked during the years of secrecy. The Bell Telephone Laboratories were one of those brought into contact with these problems. During the succeeding years at our laboratories, the research, development and preproduction model areas of work followed each other in an orderly manner. Preproduction models of the new instruments developed had been given field trials by the military people, design and production of equipment for use had been authorized and the first of the production equipment from the factories was in the hands of the proper military organizations on Pearl Harbor Day.

These instruments were used in the first battles of the Pacific war and played a more important part in our successes there during the months following Pearl Harbor. The research and development effort on this type of instrument was already under expansion at the time of Pearl Harbor and immediately thereafter its rate of expansion was enormously stepped up. This type of instrument, which was unheard of in previous wars, was used in active combat in the early battles and has since been an important element in all combat of land, sea and air.

It would not have been possible to make these instruments in their various forms available in large quantities in 1942 had not the military laboratories responsible for this type of work done such splendid exploratory work in the early thirties and then brought the industrial laboratories into full contact with the problems as early as 1938. We, therefore, owe the availability of this important new type of instrument at the war's beginning and the possibility of immediate and rapid expansion in quantity and variety to the relatively small effort of the military laboratories in the early thirties, and to the somewhat expanded effort of the military laboratories and industrial laboratories during the period from 1938 through 1940.

It is obvious that had the military people been given more adequate funds in the decade prior to 1940 and had the problem of secrecy been so handled that the industrial laboratories could have been brought into this problem earlier than in 1938, the development of these instrumentalities would have been still further advanced. Equipment could then have been available in sufficient quantity and variety prior to our entrance into the war for use by the military people for development of military tactics and personnel training.

We shall next turn to the other example which I have selected as one illustrative of a highly unfavorable situation in an important instrument of war area that came about largely through the lack of organization and limited funds in the prewar period. Instruments of war from this area, which will not be named, found limited use in the first World War. At that time, academic scientists, applied scientists from our industrial laboratories, and the military people established a new technology and new instruments for war use based upon one of the fundamental areas of physics. Soon after the last war, the pure science and industrial laboratories became dissociated from the effort of military laboratories on such instruments and were almost completely out of touch with them until our preparations for war were expanding in the months before Pearl Harbor. During the almost twenty-five years intervening, this underlying physical science had made very broad and important advances. The applied technology of this basic area had also made available instrumentalities for man's peaceful uses that were very far in advance of those of the first World War period. The techniques of measurement and experiment that had been evolved for the peacetime technology were much more numerous and precise in their nature than those of the first World War period.

When the development programs of the military laboratories of this area and the instruments of war resulting from them were examined by our pure and applied scientists in the months preceding Pearl Harbor, they found that very little progress had been made since the last war. There had been but little application of the technology that had become available in the intervening years.

Here is a most important area of warfare where there had been initial application of a field of science in World War I, yet, in the intervening twenty-five years, only limited advances had been made. Little use had been made of the great advances that had come from our pure science and industrial laboratories during this time.

A program involving pure science, industrial and military laboratories was at once organized. It was expanded as rapidly as possible. This program has been highly successful; large and important contributions to our winning the war have been and are being made. But they were not available as soon as there was need for them; the valuable time lost in the period of peace could not be regained. The useful and potent instrumentalities that could well have been developed and perfected during the peace period had to be developed, designed, field tested and produced after the war was under way.

These two examples illustrate the wide divergencies in preparedness resulting from the lack of an adequate organization to insure that all developments of military instrumentalities are taking full advantage of advances made in science and industrial technology of all areas, and the lack of adequate financial support. The postwar organization must protect us against such uneven coverage in the different sectors and insure that in all of them it is even better than that of the more favorable example I have given. It is essential that adequate funds to carry out these well organized programs be available.

In the peace years preceding the war, instruments of war researches and developments were carried out almost entirely in the laboratories of the Army and Navy and industrial laboratories. The initiative for the development and for general studies to insure that there was adequate coverage in the different areas of military instruments development was in the Army and Navy military organizations. It was their practice to assign some of the work to their own laboratories and to place the remainder by contract with industrial laboratories. In general, the tasks of the industrial laboratories were specifically assigned and these laboratories were not concerned with the broad planning of programs.

Beginning in the latter half of 1940 with the organization of the National Defense Research Committee and the expansion of preparedness activities, an increasing amount of the research for and development of instrumentalities was carried out in the laboratories of the NDRC and in the industrial laboratories. The military laboratories were increasingly concerned with establishment of requirements, control of development of components and systems and, in association with their military organizations, in field trials and application studies. Most of the pure scientists that were brought together in large numbers in the NDRC laboratories made their first contact with instruments of war problems. In order to do its research and development effectively, the NDRC found it necessary to establish through contracts, usually with universities, large laboratories of its own. These laboratories took on increasingly the character of our large industrial laboratories. They soon found it necessary to organize their efforts on a large project basis. They brought together groups composed of scientists, engineers, mechanics, draftsmen and technicians of various sorts in order effectively to carry out the type of work involved in instruments of war research and development. This pattern differed very much from that normally found in the pure research at universities during peacetime, but was quite similar to that of the industrial laboratory.

The normal work pattern in the pure science laboratory is much more on an individual than on a group or team basis. The organization of scientific, engineering and technician personnel into an effective team is rarely done. The normal set-up of the pure science laboratories at the universities is not one that is well suited for most of the instruments of war research and development. On the other hand, the normal set-up of the modern industrial laboratory, both in types of personnel available and in housing and facilities, is well adapted to such research and development activities. It is because of this fact that the industrial laboratories so rapidly and effectively converted themselves into military instrumentalities research and development units.

Based upon our experiences during the war and in the prewar years, I believe that the best places for carrying out the greater part of instruments of war research and development are the laboratories of the Army and Navy and our industrial laboratories. The laboratories of the Army and Navy have proved their worth and their ability to carry out such projects. They will need strengthening and broadening beyond their status of the prewar years, and this should be done. During the war, industrial laboratories have demonstrated their effective-

Pattern of NACA

ness in this area. They are always in intimate contact with the advances of pure science and their methodology of work is under continuous change to maintain it at the most effective state for carrying out the applied science research and development of the moment. Because of the competition between the industrial laboratories inherent in our competitive capitalistic economy, these laboratories are maintained at a high state of efficiency. The contact of the military laboratories with them will be an aid to the military laboratories in their maintenance of an effective organization for work.

The programs of the military and industrial laboratories must be given consideration by competent bodies to insure that full use is being promptly made of the advances in pure science and industrial technology and that there is an adequate program, which is carried out efficiently, in each area of military instrumentalities. There exists in the National Advisory Committee in Aeronautics, which has been in existence for many years, a pattern that might well be employed in the solution of this problem. Military instrumentalities research and development could well be divided into a few areas and a committee along the general lines of the NACA formed for each area. Such committees, chosen from the indicated areas of pure and applied science, working in close cooperation with the military organizations responsible for research and development programs, would give national insurance that the program in each of the military instrumentalities areas was adequately scientific in its nature and was taking full advantage of the advances of science and technology.

On the basis of our experience in the war and the peace years immediately preceding, I believe that such an organization of effort with an adequate provision of funds will insure a military research and development program that will keep this country at the forefront of instrumentalities preparedness, provided that secrecy requirements do not place limits upon the interchange of information and upon cooperative activities. A most essential element in the forming of a postwar program will be the solution of the requirements of secrecy in such a way that no serious limitations are placed upon the necessary interchange of information between groups working within this pattern.

Discussion: R. P. Russell

We have heard in this Forum of teamwork in research, of research teams, of research task forces.

We have also heard of the major expansion in research and development activities that this country faces. I think we can all be sure that teamwork will be even more important in the future than it has been in the past.

One of the aspects of securing such teamwork was brought out in a very interesting fashion by Dr. Jewett, when he referred to the lapwelds that join together the various parts of any successful organization. These joints must be lapwelds, they must be smooth lapwelds, and information must flow freely across them in both directions. He was speaking of the over-all organization that constitutes American industry. For the moment, I am speaking about the research organization itself.

It seems to me that not only must those lapwelds be horizontal, across the organization, but they must be vertical as well. I don't see how any research and development organization can be expected to produce worthwhile results unless the men doing the work understand the problems involved. And there is no way that I can see for them to understand those problems without that free flow of information across at all levels in the group and from one level to another. I think that is going to be one of the major problems facing every one of us who has to do with organized research in the years to come. We must see to it that the men in the organization at all levels understand what they are working for, what the problems are, in order that these problems may be solved, and in the shortest possible time. The younger men in the organization must know what the problems are not only because they won't be able to do their best work without a clear perception of their objectives but also because the setting of programs will be really sound only if their views are adequately considered in deciding what is to be done by whom and how.

As we have heard of this necessity for teamwork in research, it seems to me that there may not have been sufficient emphasis placed on the fact that every research organization, although it constitutes a team, still is only a part of a very much larger team; and without over-all industry teamwork, the whole effort must fail.

A most impressive statement along these lines appeared in a recent bulletin of the Brookings Institution, and with your indulgence I would like to quote from it:

"The achievement of higher standards of living depends basically upon the combined influence of the following factors: (1) natural and human resources; (2) scientific discoveries and inventions; (3) engineering applications; (4) business organization and management; (5) the economic system; (6) the governmental system. Scientists, inventors, engineers, business managers, and professional students of economics and government are in final analysis cooperating in a common objective—that of increasing the capacity of the people to satisfy their wants.

"Each of these groups"—and I don't think that anyone who has talked before this Forum today is entirely blameless in this respect—"likes to think of itself as of primary importance; but the sanest conception is that each group is an essential part of a larger whole. Scientific discoveries would not yield practical results if we did not have invention; patented technological apparatus and devices would be impotent were it not for engineering applications to productive processes; engineering can function in a private enterprise system only in conjunction with a business organization which appraises the feasibility of new developments in relation to other factors of production and the potentialities of profit and loss; the individual business enterprise in turn will be thwarted if the economic system is defective; and the functioning of the economic system is in turn dependent upon the character and the administration of the governmental system.

"As a result of a combination of developments, which cannot here be summarized, these various factors came to work together so effectively as to give us a century or more of phenomenal progress. As we look forward, continued advancement will depend upon the degree to which we can continue to make the inter-related parts of a complex society work effectively together."

I wish to comment briefly, also, on the subject of Secretary Patterson's address and the very stimulating discussion which followed it. Like Dr. Kelly, but in a very much narrower field than his, I also have been privileged to work with the military forces and with the National Defense Research Committee in connection with several weapons and munitions. Also, for a civilian, I have been privileged in that I have managed to see some of these products of American research and development used in anger against the enemy. Therefore, the subject of continuing in peacetime proper and adequate development of weapons and munitions is a subject that is very close to my heart.

Responsibility for Security

I think after this discussion we can all of us see that in the peacetime years to come it is absolutely essential that we in industrial research and development set aside a part—and by a part I mean an appreciable part—of our endeavors to work aggressively on the pressing technical problems involved in assuring our national security. That means the organizations, that means the men, that means the facilities, and it probably also means the money that will be required to see that this country is kept at least abreast, and if we do our job properly, kept out ahead as regards munitions and weapons of war.

POSTSCRIPT

THE FORUM recorded in this volume was an effort, perhaps the most serious up to this time, to obtain a wide cross-section of qualified opinion on the future of industrial research.

The demonstrated capacity of the nation for production and service is far above the prewar level. The new factor which formed the basis for this result is technological progress and its engineering applications. This progress in turn resulted from industrial research, more than from any other single factor. During the past twenty-five years a large segment of industry learned how to organize and plan for its own technical progress through industrial research. But industry is still far short of meeting, or fully understanding, its own needs for research, and the nation as a whole is farther from that goal. The hope was that, through the Forum, the most important areas for expansion of the industrial research effort, and the most important problems to be studied in preparation for any further expansion, would be more clearly defined.

This hope seems to have been measurably realized. While expansion is needed in industrial research, it is clear that the most important new effort must be directed to all segments of business, and that the field of national security must not be neglected in the years of peace. The most important immediate problems are training more research specialists, bringing the country as a whole to a better understanding of research,

The Crucial Problems

and working out a permanent liaison between industrial research and the military forces.

Higher standards of living and permanent security against military aggression depend upon success in meeting these needs.

THIS BOOK *was designed by Warren Chappell, New York. For the cover design he adapted a photograph by Gordon Parks of a Podbielniak Column, used for the analysis of complex mixtures of hydrocarbon gases. The book was set at Huxley House, New York, in the 11 point Linotype Janson, printed at The Southworth-Anthoensen Press and bound by John W. Marchi, both of Portland, Maine. It is printed on 60 lb. Ragston, supplied by the Stevens-Nelson Paper Corporation, Boston. The Beck Engraving Company printed the cover papers by the gravure process.*